METHUEN'S MONOGRAPHS
ON BIOLOGICAL SUBJECTS

General Editor: KENNETH MELLANBY, C.B.E.

BIOCHEMICAL ASPECTS
OF AMPHIBIAN DEVELOPMENT

Biochemical Aspects
of Amphibian Development

ELIZABETH M. DEUCHAR

LONDON: METHUEN & CO LTD
NEW YORK: JOHN WILEY & SONS INC

597.6
D485

First published in 1966
by Methuen and Co Ltd
11 New Fetter Lane, EC4
© *1966 Elizabeth Deuchar*
Printed in Great Britain by
Richard Clay (The Chaucer Press), Ltd.,
Bungay, Suffolk

Contents

Preface

As any subject develops, it broadens in scope and requires progressively larger textbooks to encompass it fully. At the same time, however, certain major features of the subject become easier to select and to summarize in smaller books which, owing to their lighter weight, lighter style and lesser expense, reach the pockets of a much wider range of readers than any of their large forerunners. Biochemical embryology owes its recognition as a subject in its own right, distinct from the background of more general embryology, mainly to Joseph Needham who wrote the first, large textbooks bringing together an immense range of facts under this subject-heading. The main achievement of his three-volume treatise, *Chemical Embryology* (1931) was to collect all the findings in logical order, with critical comment, under one (or rather, three) covers so that many people became aware of them and started trying to assess their importance. Then, in case they had not found it possible to do this in the ten subsequent years, his second great book, *Biochemistry and Morphogenesis* (1942) provided a masterly integration of the biochemical with other experimental findings and gave many interpretations of them which are still acceptable now, a quarter of a century later. We owe more, recently, to Brachet's interpretations of the subject in his two books, *Embryologie Chimique* (1944) and *The Biochemistry of Development* (1960). Their literary and factual scope is not nearly so broad as Needham's, but Brachet's long research experience embodied in these books has given a lead to our thinking, as well as summarizing important recent findings, particularly in Amphibian biochemical embryology.

It is now over five years since the publication of *The Biochemistry of Development*. These have been prolific years of research which is now being carried out by workers who benefit from a multilateral research training and from improved opportunities for interdepartmental and even international collaboration. So there is plenty more to be documented and, at the same time, since the subject has been given a more integrated structure already in the larger books just mentioned, it is now possible to compile a small and selective account of it in this, smallest book yet written on the subject of biochemical embryology. Having in mind the usual size of Methuen Monographs, it has been decided to confine this book to amphibian development, though references to work on birds have been included wherever these were considered essential for the understanding of a particular topic.

I have been severely conscious, however, of the restrictions set by the decision to be brief, and all through this book have felt aware of incompletenesses. In the attempt not to give falsely rounded accounts of each topic which would, as a result, be too superficial and uncritical, I may have tended to overstress the uncertainties and the problems still requiring investigation. This may have had the effect of making the book sound too much like a vocationary address to young, uncommitted research workers! Certainly, part of its intention is to interest biochemists in the embryological problems that need their expertise and ideas in order to be solved satisfactorily. But my primary intention is to provide an effective, small textbook that will give the advanced student and the research worker a brief, critical review of the recent findings as well as an adequate guide to further reading. It is hoped that this intention has been achieved without losing sight either of the integrity of the embryo as an organism or of the problems which those of us who were nurtured in the older environs of morphological embryology still consider to be of overriding importance.

Because this is the first book I have ever published, I am more than usually indebted to other authors, readers, and colleagues who have made it possible for me to complete it with a certain measure of confidence. I should like particularly to thank Professor J. Z. Young and Dr D. Roodyn who have each read through the whole manuscript and have managed to interpolate encouragement with their criticisms. Dr F. Billett has painstakingly read and criticized the chapters on gastrulation and neurulation. Other experts have read other chapters: Dr Ruth Bellairs and Dr J. Williams kindly read Chapter 3, Dr Sydney Smith, Chapter 4; Professor H. Tiedemann suggested several additions to Chapter 7, and Dr J. A. Tata discussed Chapter 9 with me most helpfully.

Many authors have offered to lend their original photographs, and I am indebted to numerous others for permission to copy their figures: these are all acknowledged in the text. I owe very many thanks to Mrs Jane Astafiev for the drawings and for the great rise in morale that their beauty has afforded me. For doing all the photography with care and skill, Mr A. Aldrich and Mr D. Dunn must also be thanked. Last, and probably most, I have to thank my tireless typist, Miss Eileen Tribe.

Elizabeth M. Deuchar

University College, London
September 1965

Linking Biochemistry and Morphology in the Study of Animal Embryos

Scientists of every era probably always feel that their own particular generation is witnessing a hitherto unparalleled *rapprochement* of interest between previously unrelated fields of investigation. This is not surprising, for research of any depth of penetration, in whatever era or in whatever context of knowledge it is carried out, is likely to cross conventional boundaries and to create new subject-headings of its own. There has never, for example, been any real boundary between the physico-chemical and the biological sciences: it is the scientists themselves who have tended to specialize in divergent directions. Whenever a biological analysis is carried to its lower limits, or a physico-chemical observation pursued to its upper levels of complexity, the arbitrary division between these two fields of investigation disappears.

Our own generation can rightly claim, however, to be experiencing a special kind of 'boundary-crossing' which has never occurred before. In our time, both biochemists and biologists have begun to use the same objects as starting-points for their investigations: moreover, both are now interested in studying them at the *same* level of complexity. This is largely because the biologist with his new tool, the electron microscope, has made an enormous downward jump in level of analysis. He is now able to see some of the aggregates of molecules within cells, and it is these that he describes today under the old headings of 'anatomy' and 'morphology' – instead of describing only the relatively enormous structures to which so many millions of molecules contribute that the properties of any one aggregate are obscured. The biochemists, on their side, have also modified their outlook. They have become preoccupied with the mechanisms that control intracellular metabolism by virtue of a particular macromolecular structure: for instance, the helical molecule of nucleic acid with its particular sequences of nucleotides that determine the kinds of proteins synthesized. So they have reached the moment of recognition that the structures viewed under the electron microscope are highly relevant to the processes in which they are primarily interested, at just the same time as the biologists recognize the relevance of these same structures to the features which they are accustomed to study.

Because of this common ground of interest, it might be thought that here, at last, are obvious openings for long-term collaboration between biologists and biochemists and for rapid advances in knowledge. But scientists very often remain 'shy' and limited in outlook: they still cling to their familiar background and revert to this to obtain their final criterion as to what facts are valid and important. Though the biochemist and the biologist may now share the same tools, materials, and laboratories, and even read the same books, they still do not have quite the same viewpoint. The biochemist still is not satisfied unless he can relate what he sees in an electron microscope picture ultimately to his own style of abstractions: formulae expressing dynamic chemical reactions. The biologist, looking at the same electron microscope picture, is satisfied only when he is able to relate it, like any other of his experimental observations, to the visible properties of the living, intact cells with which he was first familiar. So, the dichotomy between the scientists remains and those outstanding advances in knowledge that we hope for have not yet been achieved.

The meaning(s) of 'Molecular Embryology'

In common with other biologists, many of those who call themselves embryologists are now engaged in research that is ultimately concerned with events at the molecular level. The title 'molecular biology' is so much used nowadays as to have become a cliché. Is it, therefore, justifiable to distinguish any particular field of research as 'molecular embryology'? In my view, it is, for this term can be used in two, quite different, ways. The first is the obvious, more general one, to denote the current interest in the biochemical phenomena that occur during the development of embryos. But one may also interpret 'molecular embryology' to mean, literally, the embryology of the molecules themselves. This is a particularly interesting topic of recent research, to which increasing attention is being drawn. Some of the molecules whose structure and properties in adults are well-known have been shown to *develop* through a series of intermediate stages in embryonic tissues, before attaining these adult properties. Examples of such molecules are the 'iso-enzyme' forms of lactate dehydrogenase, and the embryonic forms of haemoglobin, about which more will be said later. These illustrate a point which should be emphasized in this introductory chapter: namely, the uniqueness of some of the biochemical events in the embryo. The embryo is, in fact, unique material for the study of certain kinds of biochemical process. In no other environment, except embryonic cells, do molecules *develop* in the way just described. In no other environment, except the embryo, is the metabolic trend so persistently in one direction, towards synthesis of increasing quantities of increasingly complex structures. For the biochemist, who so often has had to struggle to elucidate the steps in cyclical processes of metabolism in adult tissues, embryos ought, therefore, to offer a most attractive system in which to follow mainly one-way processes of synthesis, from relatively simple beginnings.

There is, however, one major complication in this synthetic milieu: the *yolk*. It is present as the main source of energy and raw materials in all embryos except those of mammals, and every major step in synthesis is preceded by yolk-breakdown. So, when dealing with these embryonic cells, the biochemist has to make sure that he can distinguish synthetic steps in the presence of catabolic processes. Very often, 'snapshot' methods of analysis have to be employed, in which a sample is taken at one particular moment, usually killing the embryo, and a judgement is made about the processes that were occurring *in vivo*, from the products that are found to be present in this material. It is often difficult to know whether these products are intermediates in yolk-breakdown, or in new protein synthesis. Similarly, when an enzyme activity is being studied, it may not be clear whether its main function *in vivo* is that of synthesis or breakdown. These difficulties have for a long time been recognized in the work on amphibian embryos that forms the subject of this book. It is not so widely realized, though, that the same is true in bird and reptile embryos too, despite the fact that so much of their yolk is extra-cellular. In these forms just as in the amphibians, the early processes of tissue formation and cell-differentiation occur at the expense of *intra*cellular yolk. It is only later that the extracellular yolk is also absorbed, via the gut and the blood stream, and its breakdown is then confined to the yolk sac cells.

The 'favourite' material

Since none of the difficulties just outlined would apply to the yolkless cells of mammalian embryos that rely on maternal secretions for nutriment, any non-embryologist must wonder why mammal embryos have not been used more often in biochemical investigations. The answer is that of expediency. These embryos are not easily accessible, and have not yet been kept alive or operated on successfully at the very early stages of their development. Mammalian experimental embryology is still only in its very beginnings.

Just the opposite is true of amphibian embryos. Their relatively large size, abundance, and the ease with which they may be observed have made them familiar objects of study from the earliest days of embryological research. Some of the classic, simple experiments, with fundamental and far-reaching implications, were performed on them and gave impetus to rapidly-growing fields of investigation. The best-known example of such 'trend-setting' is the famous ligation experiment carried out by Spemann on the newt embryo (Fig. 4.5 *a*). This led him to formulate his theory of the 'organizer' which has coloured the thinking of all embryologists throughout the sixty years since then. In fact, one of the earliest stimuli to biochemical investigations on amphibian embryos was the desire to discover the chemical 'organizer substance' believed to be responsible for 'inducing' ectoderm to develop into a neural plate. This subject will be dealt with in a later chapter.

It is because of an extensive knowledge already about the morphology and behaviour of amphibian embryonic cells, that the incentive to continue biochemical work on them has persisted. It has seemed more possible by using these familiar and much-studied forms, to make meaningful biochemical observations, which the biologist may relate to his known facts, than by using any other embryo.

One has to be careful, however, about applying too generally the biochemical findings in work done only on amphibian embryos. Basic biochemistry has grown up from work carried out to a very large extent on mammals and mammalian tissues. In cold-blooded, aquatic vertebrates, there may be a number of quite different characteristics: for instance, enzymes may have special properties in order to act efficiently at the lower body temperature. The usual general statement that the animal's metabolic rate is much lower than in warm-blooded forms means, in fact, that every reaction in every metabolic cycle must be similarly 'slowed down' by comparison with the well-known reactions in mammals. It can, of course, be said that *all* early embryos are 'aquatic' and 'poikilothermic': those of birds and mammals simply have a higher environmental temperature. But it still remains true that their metabolism is such as to accord with the environment. So the enzymes in a developing embryo of a frog are likely to have quite different re-action characteristics from those in a developing mammalian embryo.

As already indicated by the tone of this Introduction, the biochemical findings in amphibian embryos are going to be presented from the biologist's standpoint throughout this book. Their relevance to changing morphology and structure and to all that is known in visual terms about the properties of the embryonic cells will constantly be stressed. So, as a necessary preliminary, the morphological changes that occur during amphibian development will be described briefly in the next chapter.

CHAPTER TWO

An Outline Description of the Development of the Amphibian Embryo

---

The processes of embryonic development differ very little indeed between different amphibian species. The differences involve, for the most part, fine histological detail only. There are also occasional departures from the usual chronological order of events, and late stages of organ development differ slightly in different taxonomic groups, since there are minor differences in the structure of the adult organs. In this necessarily brief chapter we shall not lead into such details as these, however, but shall simply describe those main events that are relevant to the biochemical characteristics discussed in later chapters.

The descriptive account which follows will be based on one species, the South African Clawed Toad, *Xenopus laevis* (Daud), which has become increasingly popular in recent years for laboratory work. The account is based on personal observations, supplemented from the information in Nieuwkoop and Faber's *Normal Table of Xenopus laevis* (1956), which will be found an invaluable handbook by anyone using this species as research material.

Xenopus, a member of the family *Pipidae* and therefore more properly called a frog than a toad, has two unusual characteristics which are most convenient to scientists: it is aquatic all the year round and hence can easily be kept indoors in laboratory tanks, and it can be induced to breed at any time of year simply by means of hormone injection. Hence a supply of embryos can be arranged for any desired day, by injecting the adults with hormone (chorionic gonadotropin) the evening before. Moreover, the supply is usually copious – from 500 to 1,000 eggs being an average number for a spawning. The embryos develop more rapidly than other common frog species or the embryos of newts or salamanders:

6

FIG. 2.1 Stages of development of the South African Clawed Toad, *Xenopus laevis*. (From Weisz, 1945.)

(Continued overleaf)

B

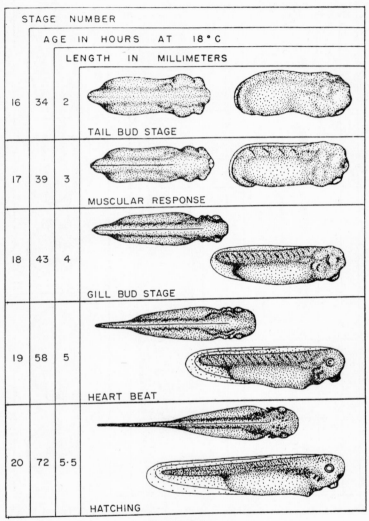

STAGE NUMBER				
	AGE IN HOURS AT 18°C			
		LENGTH IN MILLIMETERS		
16	34	2		
			TAIL BUD STAGE	
17	39	3		
			MUSCULAR RESPONSE	
18	43	4		
			GILL BUD STAGE	
19	58	5		
			HEART BEAT	
20	72	5·5		
			HATCHING	

FIG. 2.1 (*continued*)

8

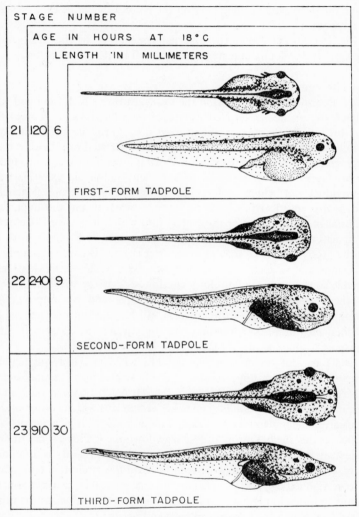

STAGE NUMBER			
	AGE IN HOURS AT 18°C		
		LENGTH IN MILLIMETERS	
21	120	6	FIRST-FORM TADPOLE
22	240	9	SECOND-FORM TADPOLE
23	910	30	THIRD-FORM TADPOLE

FIG. 2.1 (*continued*)

9

Xenopus embryos reach the early neurula stage within 18 hr, tailbud stage by 36 hr, and are hatching on the second day after they are laid, at temperatures of 18–22° C.

Fig. 2.1 (1–23) shows the external appearance of the most easily recognized developmental stages, which will be described below.

(a) The egg

After a period of growth within the ovary, during which time yolk and other materials are synthesized in the cytoplasm (see Chapter Three), the egg (or, to be more correct, the primary oocyte) ruptures the thin layer of follicle cells, escapes from the ovary, and is carried down the extremely long, coiled oviduct to the exterior. During its passage it is surrounded by two layers, each about 2 mm thick, of 'jelly', a mucoid secretion from the oviduct wall which protects the embryo from mechanical damage and is also an effective osmotic barrier between it and the hypotonic external medium (pond or tap water) into which it is shed. The exact composition of the jelly in *Xenopus* is not known, but recent work by Salthe (1963) indicates that in other frog species it consists mainly of acid mucopolysaccharides. In *Xenopus* there is an individual jelly capsule round each egg and not a continuous mass or string as is usual in other frogs and toads. Nevertheless, the eggs tend to clump together owing to the stickiness of the capsules. Within the capsule there is yet another membrane surrounding the egg itself: the extremely fine, transparent vitelline membrane.

In its natural orientation the egg lies with its darkly-pigmented, 'animal' hemisphere uppermost and the heavier, yolky 'vegetal' hemisphere shows white below this (Fig. 2.1, 1). A light spot at the animal pole indicates the position of the female pronucleus which is surrounded by clear, non-pigmented cytoplasm. The pronucleus is very near to the surface at this stage. During the passage down the oviduct, it has undergone its first meiotic (reduction) division and has extruded the first polar body, which may sometimes be seen beneath the vitelline membrane.

In section the egg is seen to have a distinct cortical layer of cytoplasm, granulated, rich in pigment, and thicker on the animal than on the vegetal side (cf. Fig. 2.2). The central parts of the egg are, for the most part, heavily packed with yolk platelets of a wide range of sizes. The majority of the larger platelets lie in the vegetal region. In the animal pole region

where there is less yolk, other cytoplasmic constituents such as mitochondria, Golgi body and endoplasmic reticulum can be identified. In
the vegetal region there are also some patches of relatively yolk-free
cytoplasm, among them the *germinal plasm* which later becomes included in the germ cells that migrate to the embryonic gonads. Blackler
(1958) has followed the fate of this plasm in *Xenopus*, and similar plasm

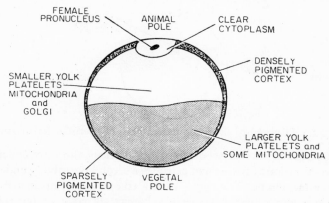

FIG. 2.2 Section through oocyte stage of *Xenopus laevis*.
(Diagrammatic.)

has been described in other frog species by Bounoure (1939). The
arrangement of the cytoplasm is mainly completed after fertilization,
and some final shifts occur just before gastrulation.

(b) Fertilization

Since in *Xenopus* fertilization occurs after the egg is laid, the sperm has
to penetrate both jelly coats as well as the vitelline membrane. The
mechanism of penetration has not been investigated, but is thought to
be due at least partly to enzyme action. There are two immediate effects
of sperm penetration in amphibians: one is that the vitelline membrane
becomes impermeable to other spermatozoa, and the other is that a *grey
crescent* forms, and marks the future dorsal side of the egg, as a result of
a shift of cortical pigment towards the animal pole on this side. Usually
this crescent appears on the side opposite to the point of sperm entry
and has a definite orientation in relation to the 'copulation path' followed

by the sperm as it moves towards the female pronucleus to fuse with it (Fig. 2.3). There are, however, exceptions to this orientation, and the position of the grey crescent can be modified experimentally in some frog species by procedures such as rotating the egg so that its sub-cortical contents shift under the action of gravity.

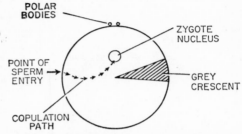

FIG. 2.3 Diagram to show copulation path of sperm at fertilization.

Before the sperm reaches the female pronucleus, the latter undergoes its second meiotic division and extrudes a second polar body under the vitelline membrane. The egg is then a true *ovum*, as distinct from a secondary oocyte and, once fertilized, may correctly be termed the *zygote*. (This terminology is all too frequently misused: medical anatomists sometimes even refer to the human *embryo*, much later in its development, as an 'ovum'!)

(c) Cleavage

This first phase of embryonic development is so named because its chief feature is the gradual subdivision, or 'cleavage', of the original zygote from one cell into several thousand cells. This happens according to a particular pattern characteristic of each species, and in amphibians, as in most vertebrates, the initial cleavage pattern is usually described as 'radial'. Since, however, the first cleavage passes through the centre of the grey crescent and thus divides the embryo into right and left halves, some authors prefer to call it 'bilateral' cleavage. At each cleavage the nucleus divides mitotically and a new cell membrane eventually completes itself between the daughter cells, across the plane in which the metaphase plate of the nuclear division lay. The furrows seen externally at each division (Fig. 2.1, 3–7) are caused by a contraction and also inward penetration of part of the cortex. In cinematographs of this process, on the dorsal side pigment granules can be seen to move towards the furrow, then later, new cortical substance is synthesized and emerges at the base of the furrow, usually appearing white owing to absence of pigment, while at the same time the furrow becomes less pronounced. These features have been described in the newt and the axolotl by Selman and Waddington (1955), and Zotin (1964).

Normally the first two cleavages are meridional and the third one horizontal (Fig. 2.1, 3–5). At the four-cell stage, the cells of the dorsal side are noticeably smaller than the ventral ones and in subsequent cleavages the animal pole cells are smaller than those of the vegetal pole.

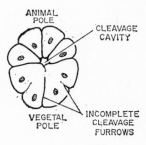

FIG. 2.4 Section of morula stage, showing cleavage cavity and incomplete division of vegetal cells. (Diagrammatic.)

The fourth cleavage is meridional and the fifth one horizontal. All the cells divide synchronously at these early stages. The resultant, 16–64-cell stage embryos are usually called 'morulae'. These stages are distinct from the later, blastula stage, in that they consist of a solid ball of cells, without any extensive internal cavity. There is, however, a gradually enlarging *cleavage cavity* centrally, from the 4-cell stage onwards, since the inner surfaces of the blastomeres do not cohere at their animal pole ends. At the vegetal pole, it may be noted that divisions are often not yet complete by the time the next cleavage has already started (Fig. 2.4).

From the 64-cell stage onwards, vegetal pole cells cleave distinctly more slowly than those at the animal pole: a common feature in heavily-yolked animal embryos. Though it is often stated that the slower cleavage is *due to* the higher yolk content of the vegetal cells, it should be noted that there is no experimental proof that yolk as such has any effect on cleavage rate. On the contrary, large quantities of yolk have been removed by puncture without effect on the cleavage pattern (Waddington, 1952). The arrangement of blastomeres has also been altered by various procedures, including superimposition of two two-cell stage embryos which then fuse into one (Mangold and Seidel, 1927). Such experiments as these have shown that the cleavage pattern of the amphibian egg can readily be modified without deleterious effects on the embryo, despite the fact that, in embryos that are not experimentally tampered with, this pattern is so consistent. The factors that control the events of cleavage in amphibian embryos will be discussed in Chapter Four.

(d) The Blastula

This might be termed the 'hollow ball' stage of development. As a result of the faster cleavages in the animal hemisphere, these smaller, animal pole cells come to lie as a relatively thin layer above the large vegetal

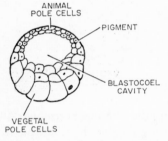

FIG. 2.5 Section through blastula stage. (Diagrammatic.)

pole cells, with a sizeable cavity, called the blastocoel cavity, between them (Fig. 2.5). This cavity has arisen from the cleavage cavity mentioned earlier and is filled with fluid that must be presumed to be secreted by the cells surrounding the cavity. There has been no experimental demonstration of the origin of the blastocoel fluid, however, and in some species it has a distinctly higher pH than that of the cells (see Needham, 1931; Stableford, 1949).

In *Xenopus* the animal pole cells roofing the blastocoel divide tangentially to form two layers, the outer of which contains most of the cortical material. Movements of intracellular materials and shifts in relative position of the animal and vegetal pole cells also occur: these have been called 'pregastrulation' movements since they are a necessary prelude to the much larger, morphogenetic movements of gastrulation itself. There is, first, an upward streaming of cytoplasm from the outer ends of the vegetal pole cells towards their interior ends (Fig. 2.6). This movement has also been demonstrated in other species by Schechtman (1935), Nicholas (1945) and Harris (1964), who placed patches of dye on the ventral surface of the blastula and were able to observe its inward progress. In *Xenopus* the pregastrulation movements include also a downward spreading of animal pole cells over those of the vegetal pole. As a result, some of the future mesoderm cells are already below the surface dorsally before gastrulation begins: quite unlike other amphibians. *Xenopus* is exceptional in this particular feature, which was

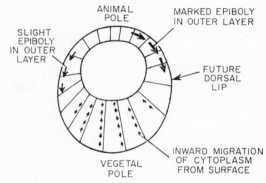

FIG. 2.6 Diagram to show pre-gastrulation movements.

pointed out by Nieuwkoop and Florschütz (1950). This point needs to be borne in mind when comparing biochemical data obtained at the beginning of gastrulation in *Xenopus* (i.e. *after* some mesoderm is already inside) with those obtained on other species.

The dyeing method used to trace movements of cytoplasm in the blastula has also been widely employed in order to follow the movements and fates of various groups of cells later. As a result of such work, it has been possible to compile what are known as 'fate maps' indicating the areas on the surface of the blastula that are destined to form each of the main tissue and organ systems of the body (see Fig. 2.7, from the diagrams of Pasteels (1940) who was one of the leaders in this work). It has long been customary to distinguish three 'germ layers' in the early embryo: *ectoderm*, *mesoderm*, and *endoderm*. Normally, the outer layer,

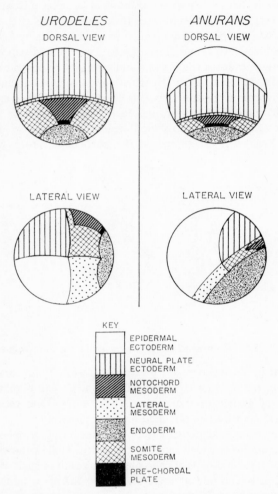

FIG. 2.7 'Fate maps' of blastula areas destined to form various embryonic tissues. (After Pasteels, 1940.)

ectoderm, gives rise to epidermis of the skin, and derivatives of it, as well as to the nervous system (the neural plate ectoderm). *Mesoderm*, the intermediate layer, forms muscle, skeleton, connective tissue, and vascular system, while *endoderm*, which comes to be the innermost layer, gives rise to the gut epithelium and also to the germ cells. Cells of all these germ layers abut onto the surface of the embryo at the blastula stage, and it is the morphogenetic movements of gastrulation (see below) that bring the three layers into their definite topographical relationships. When the relationships are altered experimentally, however, the cells show great adaptability and it should be emphasized that their fates are not rigidly determined until much later in development.

(e) Gastrulation

The phase of development called gastrulation is characterized by large-scale tissue movements known as 'morphogenetic movements'. These consist, in amphibians, of two main processes: *invagination*, the inward movement of mesoderm and endoderm round the lips of a groove known as the *blastopore*, and *epiboly*, the stretching and overgrowth of these two layers by the ectoderm, which eventually covers the whole surface of the embryo. Externally, the progress of gastrulation is evident from the appearance and changing contour of the blastopore groove. As seen in Fig. 2.1 (8–10), the blastopore appears first as a small, darkly pigmented line at the mid-dorsal point of the embryo, at the border of the area derived from the original grey crescent. The line then spreads laterally to form first a crescentic, then a circular groove around the margins of which cells are continually passing into the interior of the embryo. The circular groove diminishes in size as the mass of endoderm that invaginates last is gradually withdrawn from its centre.

In longitudinal section (Fig. 2.8) it is seen that the cells that invaginate dorsally extend inwards beneath the dorsal ectoderm of the embryo until they reach its anterior end and so form a complete roof to the new internal cavity or *archenteron* (future gut cavity) which is formed behind the invaginating layer as it advances inwards. These archenteron roof tissues form the notochord and somites. The tissues that invaginate laterally, somewhat later but in continuity with the dorsal tissues, represent lateral mesoderm that forms kidney, body wall, vascular system, gut musculature, and mesenteries. Endoderm invaginates ventrally. The blastocoel cavity is gradually obliterated as the gut cavity enlarges. Finally, with the withdrawal of the 'yolk plug' of endoderm and the closure of the blastopore, the process of gastrulation is complete (see Fig. 2.8 c).

The old, conventional idea of the gastrula as a 'three-layered stage' comparable in all animal embryos, has to be considered with caution in amphibians. In the tailed forms (Urodeles) there is no endoderm dorsally at the end of gastrulation: it spreads round beneath the dorsal

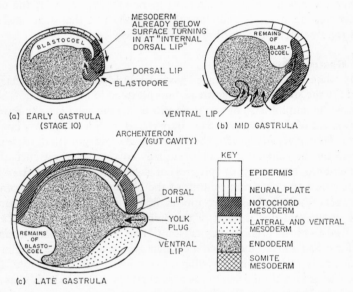

FIG. 2.8 (a–c) Stages of gastrulation, seen in longitudinal section. (Diagrammatic.) Arrows indicate main tissue movements.

mesoderm slightly later. In Anurans (frogs and toads, including *Xenopus*), on the other hand, the gut cavity is from the first roofed with endoderm as well as mesoderm, because these two layers invaginate overlapping (see Fig. 2.9). The lateral and ventral walls of the gastrula are not three-layered in any of the amphibian forms until the ventral mesoderm has fully spread inwards between endoderm and ectoderm. There are then only two points left where mesoderm does not intervene between endoderm and ectoderm: the future oral membrane over the mouth, and the future anal membrane over the anus. Both these membranes break down after hatching, when the gut becomes functional.

The adaptability of gastrula cells under experimental conditions has already been mentioned. This needs re-emphasizing, because it means

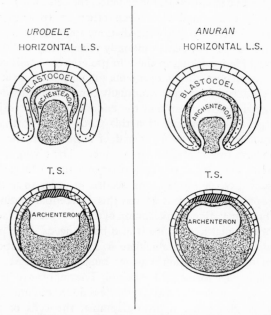

Fig. 2.9 Anuran (Frog or Toad) and Urodele (Newt or Salamander) gastrulae seen in horizontal section, to show overlapping of mesoderm and endoderm. Conventions as in Figs. 2.7 and 2.8.

that the onus lies on biochemical investigators to discover mechanisms of differentiation that can be re-directed and modified at several of their successive steps. One of the ways in which the gastrula cells of different germ layers manifest their differences is by their types of movement: thus, mesoderm and endoderm have a tendency to invaginate inside ectoderm, and ectoderm tends to spread out round them. They show these same, characteristic properties when isolated in small groups. When one germ layer is converted into another, in experimental conditions, the motile behaviour is also converted into that characteristic of the other germ layer. It is sometimes difficult to judge which is cause and which is effect, however. Clearly there must be some biochemical basis for these characteristic differences, but they remain unelucidated so far. Another, still more puzzling, characteristic of these cells is that they have selective affinities. If, for instance, the cells of a whole blastula are completely dissociated from each other by treatment with the chelating agent 'versene' (ethylene-diamine-tetra-acetic acid) and are then returned to normal saline, randomly mixed, they will sort out and find their own kind, sticking to these in preference to cells of the other germ layers. Moreover, their movements and adhesions are so organized that the original ectoderm cells eventually come to lie outside, with the mesoderm cells next to them and the endoderm on the inside. Curtis (1961) has produced evidence that this mode of reassortment results from different *rates* of movement and of adhesion in the three cell-types. Endoderm can be made to arrive outside, by giving it a 'start' on the other cells, allowing it to begin re-aggregation 4 hr earlier. Much further biochemical investigation is needed in order to find out what intrinsic properties of the cells govern this differential motility.

Yet another interesting manifestation of the gastrula cells' adaptability should be mentioned here, since it also badly needs some penetrating biochemical investigation to elucidate it. Parts of the embryo have a tendency to form in isolation a wider range of structures than they would normally have formed if left *in situ*. They appear to 'try to' make as complete an organism as possible, in the reduced circumstances. This means that besides being highly adaptable, the cells of the isolate establish some mutual interaction which causes them to *diverge* in their course of differentiation, instead of all forming similar tissue as they would have in the embryo. It is, of course, well known that in the intact embryo certain adjacent tissues interact and influence each other's development: the best-known example of this, which will be dealt with in a later chapter, is neural induction (the effect of dorsal mesoderm on the ectoderm overlying it, causing it to form neural plate). But these tissue interactions involve distinct cell groups acting on other, *different*, cell-groups. The situation is quite unlike this, in the isolate, where cells that would all have been similar are now reorganized to become divergent: it requires some quite separate explanation.

In conclusion, it may be pointed out that one of the important results of gastrulation is that it brings into close proximity groups of cells that were nowhere near each other in the blastula: thus, new tissue inter-actions become possible. There are also some tissue interactions that take place during gastrulation itself, with the result that some of the plasticity of the cells concerned is lost by the late gastrula stage. Other cells, however, remain plastic or, in embryological terminology, 'un-determined' until much later stages.

(f) Neurulation

The term 'neurulation' is applied to the phase of development, immedi-ately following gastrulation, in which the *neural plate* appears and folds up longitudinally to form a tube, the *neural tube*, which develops into the brain and spinal cord. The neural plate is visible externally as a

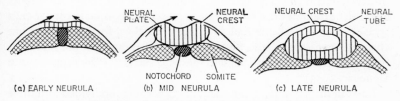

FIG. 2.10 Folding of neural plate during neurulation: seen in transverse section.

somewhat slipper-shaped, lightly-pigmented region of dorsal ectoderm (Fig. 2.1, 12). Its caudal margin just encompasses the disappearing blastopore and its cranial margin, which is much broader, lies on the ventral surface of the future head region. All the margins of the neural plate soon become thickened to form the *neural folds*. A midline groove also appears – the *neural groove*, beneath which the notochord mesoderm lies quite firmly attached (Fig. 2.1, 13, and 2.10).

As neurulation proceeds, the lateral neural folds converge towards the midline until they make contact with each other. Finally they fuse completely, thus forming a neural tube in place of the neural plate. The epidermis which has also converged towards the midline, in contact with the folds, eventually roofs over them so that the neural tube is submerged from the surface. The complete sequence of events, which is best seen in transverse section, is illustrated in Fig. 2.10.

Other dorsal axial tissues also undergo changes during neurulation: for instance, the notochord becomes distinct from somite mesoderm and forms a cylindrical rod in the midline. The somite mesoderm thickens and becomes triangular in cross-section, so that the individual somite blocks, when they segregate later, are prism-shaped. They are arranged segmentally – i.e. there is one pair of somite blocks per 'segment' of the body.

(g) Segmental structures in tailbud and larval stages

It is a feature of all vertebrates and many invertebrates that the axial structures develop in serially-repeated units which correspond to a 'segmental' pattern that is comparable in many animal forms. The pattern is particularly clear in the embyro, but is often obscured later in development as specializations, different for each taxonomic group, arise. In vertebrates the number of body segments is constant for each species: it is remarkable that the somite number, for instance, is unchanged even when large portions of dorsal mesoderm are added or removed experimentally at late gastrula stages (Waddington and Deuchar, 1953).

Later in their development, the somites become subdivided into three main components: an outer, dermatome layer which contributes to the dermis of the skin; a myotome layer which forms the dorsal muscles as well as, possibly, body wall muscles and limb muscles; and an inner, sclerotome layer that forms the elements of the vertebrae. We shall not enter into any details here about the development of the axial skeleton, but in the present context it may be noted that the vertebrae are arranged *inter*-segmentally and that each receives sclerotome cells from two adjacent segments.

The phenomenon of segmentation is exhibited, temporarily, in other mesoderm tissues such as the kidney, where there is one tubule per segment, and in the vascular system, where the branches of the dorsal aorta are at first arranged intersegmentally.

Another segmented structure that should be mentioned is the *neural crest*. At the end of neurulation two longitudinal strands of tissue become detached from the zone of the neural folds, and are known as the neural crest (Fig. 2.10). The strands later break up into segmental groups and migrate ventrally and laterally along the inner and outer margins of the somites, to give rise to a variety of structures. The fate of the neural crest cells in amphibians has been traced in numerous, painstaking experiments in which parts of the crest were removed and the resultant defect observed, or grafts of identifiable crest cells were made into hosts of another species. Much of this work was done by Hörstadius and Sellman (see Hörstadius, 1950). There are some points of uncertainty still, besides the possibility of variations in different vertebrate groups. It can be said, however, that the neural crest cells certainly give rise to the segmentally-arranged spinal ganglia, as well as to melanophores throughout the skin. They also contribute, though perhaps not exclusively, to the inner protective meninges (pia and arachnoid) of the brain and spinal cord, to the Schwann cells that en-sheath nerve fibres and secrete myelin, to some ganglion cells of the autonomic nervous system and to the adrenal medulla. In the head region, besides contributing to tooth rudiments, they have a surprising additional fate, forming most of the visceral cartilages. Because of this, there have been arguments among the traditionalists as to whether the neural crest should be counted as ectoderm or mesoderm. Clearly it offers an excellent example of the adaptability of the germ-layers. There is a point of special variation in *Xenopus*, which should be mentioned: Stevens (1954) has observed that the melanophores of the head are not derived from neural crest, but from neural plate, in this species.

The brain and spinal cord themselves show serial protuberances which have been thought to represent a kind of segmentation. These protuberances, called 'neuromeres', are the result of local mitotic activity as well as of migrations of cells, and their positions are related to the eventual arrangement of neurons in the brain and cord. But they do *not* correspond in any regular way with the body segments. Never-theless, they seem to depend for their development on the segmentation of the somite mesoderm, for Kallén (1956) found deficiencies of neuromery after removing this mesoderm from its contact with the neural plate. But the relevance of neuromery to body segmentation is made even more doubtful by its transitory nature: the protuberances very soon disappear in all types of embryos studied.

C

(h) Organ and tissue development in hatching and early larval stages

Only the briefest of accounts will be given here of the later development of tissues and organs: for details the reader is referred to Nieuwkoop and Faber's book. Special topics on which there are biochemical findings to discuss will, of course, receive further mention in later chapters.

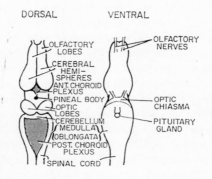

(a) EXTERNAL VIEWS

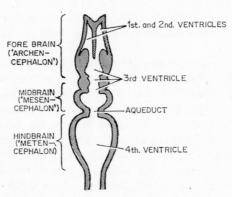

(b) MEDIAN HORIZONTAL SECTION

FIG. 2.11 Simplified drawings to show main external and internal features of the amphibian brain. Based on Grove and Newell (1944).

(i) *The nervous system*

As soon as neurulation is complete, it is already possible to distinguish two regions in the brain, called rather cumbersomely the 'archencephalon' (which represents future forebrain) and the 'deuterencephalon' (representing midbrain and hindbrain). Very soon, *three* distinct regions, fore-, mid-, and hindbrain become visible as their internal cavities enlarge. According to the usual pattern in vertebrates, the forebrain is paired, with a pair of internal cavities known as the 1st and 2nd ventricles. These communicate with the narrower, median 3rd ventricle of the midbrain, which in turn leads into the 4th ventricle of the hindbrain (Fig. 2.11).

In the forebrain region the cerebral hemispheres (very small, in amphibians), the olfactory lobes (which later fuse to become a single lobe, in *Xenopus*), the pineal and pituitary glands, and the eyes, develop (Fig. 2.11). The most important structures of the midbrain are the optic centres. In the hindbrain the cerebellum and rhombencephalon are the most prominent regions. Cranial nerve ganglia lie on the surface of the rhombencephalon, and fibres from them send connexions to hindbrain nuclei.

The early spinal cord in all vertebrate embryos comes to have three main layers: the ependymal, mantle, and marginal layers. The nuclei of the original, columnar-shaped neural tube cells accumulate medially next the central canal, and this becomes the zone of mitosis, or *ependymal layer*. As the cells differentiate into either neurons or neuroglia they become detached from this inner layer and migrate outwards into the zone, which becomes the *mantle layer*, of 'grey matter' (cell bodies). The nerve fibres that grow out peripherally from these cell bodies form the white matter of the *marginal layer*. The mantle layer consists of distinct dorsal and ventral 'horns' of grey matter. The dorsal horns are made up of sensory neurons and the ventral horns of motor neurons, which develop slightly in advance of the sensory ones. Neurons of the autonomic nervous system lie in the lateral sector of each horn, while the somatic neurons lie in the extreme dorsal and extreme ventral sectors, respectively (Fig. 2.12 *a*).

Two particular types of giant neuron, peculiar to amphibians and fish, require special mention: the Rohon–Beard cells and the Mauthner neurons. The Rohon–Beard cells are the earliest type of neuron to

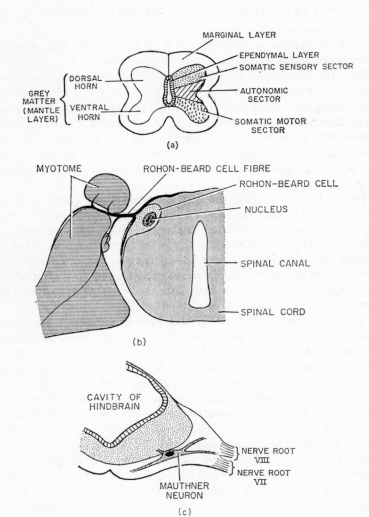

FIG. 2.12 Features of the spinal cord. (*a*) Diagrammatic transverse section to show the main layers and zones; (*b*) Sketch to show position and size of a Rohon–Beard cell (after Coghill, 1914); (*c*) Sketch of hindbrain region with a Mauthner neuron (after Herrick, 1914).

develop and are derived from the neural crest (see Hörstadius, 1950). They lie in dorsal regions of the trunk and tail spinal cord. Their axons extend longitudinally in a dorsolateral sensory tract (Fig. 2.12 *b*). Their existence is transitory, however, for they have disappeared by the time the spinal ganglia are present, and their mode of function is still uncertain. The Mauthner neurons are situated in the hindbrain of the larva (Fig. 2.12 *c*) and have extensive longitudinal connexions which provide the co-ordination for some of the very rapid swimming movements. At metamorphosis, these cells degenerate. It is probable that much more will soon be known of their functions and metabolism, since their large size enables microchemical studies to be made on single Mauthner cells (see Chapter Nine).

(ii) Special sense organs: the eye
The eye rudiments are first visible in the late neurula stage, as slight lateral protuberances of the anterior neural folds (Fig. 2.1, 15). After the closure of the neural tube, they come to lie ventrolaterally as a pair of vesicles attached to the forebrain by stalks (the optic stalks). Each vesicle grows out to make contact with the epidermis, which it then *induces* to form a lens (see later, Chapter Eight). Subsequently, the distal half of the optic vesicle retracts from the surface and invaginates into the proximal half, thus forming a two-layered 'optic cup' (Fig. 2.13). The invagination also involves the optic stalk region, which is destined to form the optic nerve. In the optic cup, the inner layer will form neural retina and the outer layer, pigmented retina: the fates of these layers are not fixed, however, until their histological differentiation has begun: they may be interchanged experimentally.

While the optic cup invaginates, the lens-forming cells of the epidermis also invaginate, forming a lens vesicle which then detaches from the surface. It is converted into a lens proper, in later larval life, by elongation of its proximal cells which form lens fibres, while the distal cells form lens epithelium. The margin of the eye cup also undergoes considerable differentiation to form the iris, ciliary and pupillary muscles. The neural retina acquires its several layers of cells in sequence and the innermost, ganglion cells send fibres down the optic stalk, which gradually loses its lumen and acquires the structure of the optic nerve. Within the eye cup, the vitreous humour forms probably as a

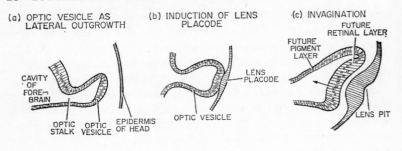

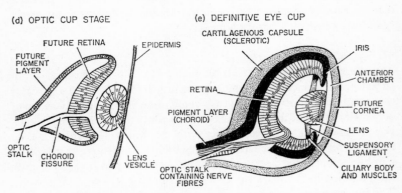

FIG. 2.13 Diagrams illustrating the development of the eye cup
and lens. (a)–(e) successive stages.

combined product of ectoderm and mesoderm cells, while the anterior
chamber, filled with aqueous humour which is presumably a secretion
from the mesoderm cells lining it, appears in front of the lens, between
it and the cornea.

Further details of the eye's structure are gradually added during
larval life and completed at metamorphosis (see Chapter Nine). Its
protective covering, the sclerotic, develops from mesoderm surrounding
the optic cup.

(iii) The ear
The rudiment of the inner ear labyrinth appears in the same way as
some of the cranial ganglion rudiments and the nasal rudiments: as a

thickened epidermal 'placode' on the surface of the head. In the case of the ear vesicle, this placode invaginates and detaches from the surface. It later becomes subdivided into utricular and saccular portions, and the three semicircular canals develop as shelf-like outgrowths from it. In the centre of each outgrowth, the cells degenerate so that looped canals result (Fig. 2.14). The structure becomes surrounded by cartilage of the otic capsule, which forms from adjacent mesenchyme. There is communication with the interior of the skull capsule via the endo-lymphatic duct, ending in the saccus endolymphaticus. Communication with vibrations from the outside world is effected, in the adult frog, by the columella cartilage abutting on to the ear drum, which is exposed on the surface of the head in amphibians.

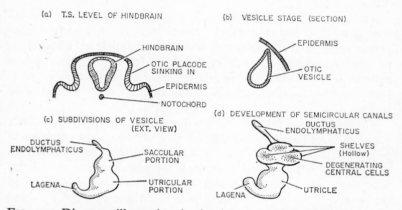

FIG. 2.14 Diagrams illustrating the development of the inner ear. (a)–(d) successive stages, (a) and (b) in section, (c) and (d) external views.

(*iv*) *Connective tissue, muscle, and skeleton*
The rudiments of these structures will be named here, but their develop-ment is an event mainly of post-embryonic stages and will not, therefore, be considered in detail.

It is logical to begin with the notochord, since this is the earliest sup-porting structure to develop in embryos, though it later degenerates and gives place to other supporting tissues. Its particular interest to the earlier embryologists was its role in influencing the early differentiation of tissues adjacent to it in the gastrula and neurula: however, at later stages it is probable that its main function is more related to biochemical events such as the laying down of early embryonic collagen. Autoradiographic work with tritium-labelled proline as 'marker' for collagen, as well as biochemical extraction methods, indicate that the notochord sheath cells (which remain alive after its central cells have vacuolated and died) are the first to accumulate collagen precursors, and a little later the sclerotome cells surrounding this sheath acquire collagen too (Deuchar, 1964). These cells form the vertebral centra, which later expand inwards to obliterate the notochord so that its remains are represented in the adult only by intervertebral material (e.g. the intervertebral discs and the nuclear pulposus of mammals).

The remainder of the skeletal elements of the body, with the exception of those formed from the neural crest, are derived from condensations of mesenchyme cells. These also accumulate labelled proline, presumably present as hydroxyproline, which is the characteristic amino-acid of collagen. Similar proline and/or hydroxyproline accumulation may be observed in the dermis of the skin, but not until larval stages.

The epidermis of the early larva is double, with an outer, expendable periderm layer beneath which the stratum germinativum continues to proliferate. The epithelia of fins, balancers, tentacles, and oral cement gland are derivatives of this layer, while the mesoderm also contributes to all these structures. At metamorphosis, certain changes take place in the larval skin, which will be dealt with in Chapter Nine.

(v) *The tail*

The tail arises from a knob of undifferentiated cells, the tailbud, visible at the end of neurulation (Pasteels, 1943). It is prominent and protrudes ventrally at first at the so-called 'tailbud stage' of embryonic development, then it grows out into a horizontal position just before hatching. The fin which develops is dependent on the integrity of the central tail tissues for its proper differentiation.

A special section (Chapter Nine) will be devoted to the later development and regenerative powers of the tail and to its final regression at metamorphosis in Anurans.

(vi) The gut

It is customary to define three regions of the embryonic gut: foregut, midgut, and hindgut. The foregut forms the pharynx, oesophagus, stomach, and the upper part of the intestine: the midgut forms the main part of the intestine, which becomes coiled in a close spiral in frog

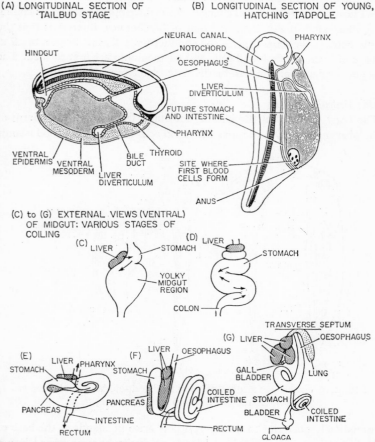

FIG. 2.15 Diagrams illustrating the development of the gut in an amphibian tadpole. (A) and (B) based on Rugh (1951); (C–G) redrawn from Nelsen (1953).

larvae. The lower part of the intestine represents the hindgut and opens to the exterior via the ectoderm-lined anus, which perforates some days after hatching, at the time when, in *Xenopus*, filter feeding gives place to the intake of solid matter. As noted already, all of the gut epithelium is endodermal in origin except the extreme anal and oral ends: its muscle and connective tissue are mesodermal, however.

The main morphological changes in the developing gut and its coiling are illustrated in Fig. 2.15. A point of biochemical interest is that the yolk persists for some time in the endodermal cells and longest of all in those of liver, where blood cells and haemoglobin are first formed. The origins of haemoglobin will be discussed later (Chapter Eight).

(vii) Vascular system

The *heart* develops at the late tailbud stage, from lateral mesoderm of the pharyngeal region. Besides the blood cells that form in blood islands

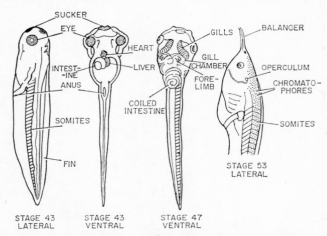

FIG. 2.16 External features of advanced tadpole stages of *Xenopus laevis*. (After Nieuwkoop and Faber, 1956.)

immediately posterior to the liver, others arise in islands at the base of the tail (Fig. 2.16). The blood islands gradually become linked into a network of vessels, forming in mesenchyme at various points throughout the body. The networks give place to larger vessels, and blood begins to circulate in these as soon as the heart muscles are active, at the late tailbud stage. (A simple plan of the main arteries of the vascular system is given in Fig. 9.1.) The blood cells acquire a form of haemoglobin which has a different structure from that of the adult (see Chapter Nine).

(viii) Hatching and larval life

Hatching is effected chemically as well as mechanically: enzymic secretions partially liquefy the jelly capsule, at the same time as the larva's wriggling movements, made possible by the development of its somitic musculature, help to free it from the capsule. Hatching does not occur successfully in poorly oxygenated water. After emergence the larvae remain for several hours immobile on the bottom and will then swim up to the surface of the water and dangle from it by a mucus thread secreted by the oral cement gland. This thread can be retracted into the pharynx at will, and acts as a filter-feeding mechanism. After one day of this habit, the larvae detach and become free-swimming, detritus feeders.

Some of the characteristic external features of *Xenopus* larvae are illustrated in Fig. 2.16 and will not be described in any further detail since they are seldom referred to in discussions of larval metabolism. By far the most radical and rapid changes in the metabolism of developing amphibians occur at metamorphosis, and are under endocrine control from the pituitary and thyroid glands. Some of the hormonal influences will be discussed in Chapter Nine.

This brief account of the embryonic development of *Xenopus laevis* has covered the main processes of development that are common features of all amphibians. Many of the morphological changes that have been described have interesting biochemical accompaniments, and these will be dealt with in the chapters that follow.

CHAPTER THREE

The Egg: its Formation, Constitution and Fertilization

In all vertebrates, synthesis of the constituents of the future egg is completed within the ovary at the *primary oocyte* stage which still has the diploid chromosome number (see Fig. 3.1). Amphibian oocytes increase enormously in size during this period of synthesis (Fig. 3.2): in *Xenopus laevis*, for instance, there is an increase in diameter from 50μ to 1 mm. The follicle cells which surround the oocyte are, on the other hand, extremely small (Fig. 3.3). They are arranged in a thin, tightly-clinging layer that is difficult to dissect off, whereas it is, on the other hand, easy to isolate the oocyte nucleus ('germinal vesicle') by dissection because it is so large as to be visible to the naked eye and is also very robust. This has made it possible to carry out biochemical studies not only on the isolated germinal vesicle, but also on the enucleated cytoplasm. One of the most remarkable discoveries has been that the cytoplasm itself contains deoxyribonucleotides of high molecular weight (Hoff-Jørgensen and Zeuthen, 1952). More will be said in a later chapter about this important finding which has contradicted previous ideas about the constancy of the DNA content per cell.

The process of oogenesis, which begins with growth of the primary oocyte, has been followed in detail in amphibians by cytological, cyto-chemical, electron microscopic, and biochemical methods. References to this work and also to the more extensive investigations on invertebrates will be found in Raven's book (*Oogenesis*, 1961). The present chapter will be limited to a discussion of some of the main problems and findings in amphibia, including the source of nutriment for the developing oocyte, the sites of yolk and pigment synthesis, the nature and

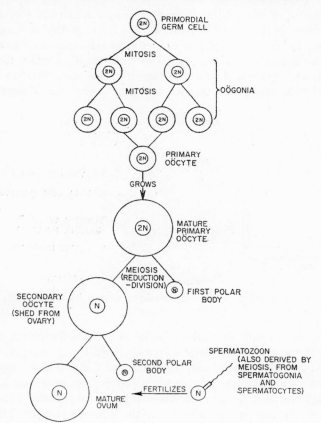

FIG. 3.1 Diagram of the maturation divisions (mitotic and meiotic) during oogenesis. 2N = diploid, N = haploid chromosome number. (Based on Grove and Newell, 1944.)

peculiarities of other components of cytoplasm and nucleus, and the changes that occur at fertilization.

(a) Nutrition of the developing oocyte

The raw materials with which the oocytes, like all other cells in the body, are nourished circulate to them in the blood stream. These materials have to reach the oocytes via ovarian tissue and follicle cells.

It is not at all clear in what form they pass across the several cell membranes in their path (for further discussion of this problem, see Brachet, 1960). Whole proteins cannot cross cell boundaries intact, as far as we know, except by a process of 'pinocytosis' in which they are actively engulfed into a pocket of the cell membrane. Pinocytosis has not yet been shown with certainty to occur in the cells of amphibian

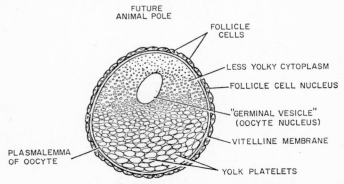

FIG. 3.3 Section of amphibian oocyte within its follicle cells. (Diagrammatic.)

ovaries, but recently Wartenberg (1964) has obtained evidence that it occurs in the oocyte. Serological investigations (e.g. Flickinger, 1960; Glass, 1959) have shown, too, that certain of the amphibian egg yolk proteins are identical to maternal blood proteins. So, unless we assume that they are taken up by pinocytosis, it has to be postulated that the oocyte synthesizes proteins identical to the maternal proteins. There is as yet no evidence either for or against this possibility. Certainly, the oocyte must possess the genetic information enabling it to carry out such syntheses. The fate of the maternal protein and the form in which it enters the oocyte clearly need much more investigation in amphibians; far more is known about this in birds (see Bellairs, 1964). The means of investigation are now readily available: protein labelling with fluorescent antibodies is now a standard method for tracing identifiable proteins into cells. (For the original method, see Coons and Kaplan, 1950.) Nace and Lavin (1964) and Lavin (1963) have used such methods to identify an antigen ('F') in the egg cortex in *Rana pipiens*. They have

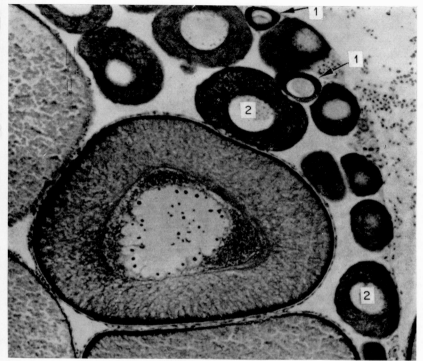

FIG. 3.2 Photograph of section through part of the ovary in *Xenopus laevis* showing the oocytes at various stages of growth. (From Wartenberg, 1962, by kind permission of the author.)

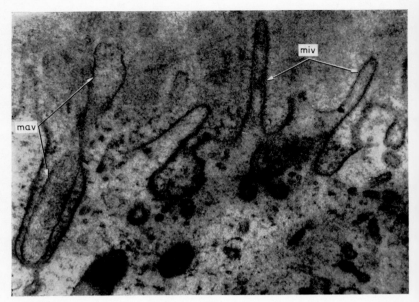

FIG. 3.4 Electron micrograph showing boundaries between the oocyte and its follicle cells. Microvilli (miv) from oocyte indent follicle cells and macrovilli (mav) from follicle cells indent outer layer of oocyte. (From Hope *et al.*, 1963, by kind permission.)

evidence that this may be present in the follicle cells too, but so far have not demonstrated its passage from these cells into the egg.

Flickinger (1960 loc. cit.) has observed proteins identical to those of the egg yolk in the liver of the female frog. It should be noted, however, that in amphibians the liver cells *retain* their *embryonic* yolk for longer than do the cells of other organs. Flickinger may, therefore, have been detecting remnants of the yolk proteins of the previous generation. It is also to be expected that some of the blood proteins will be similar to liver proteins, since the liver is the main haemopoietic organ in pre-metamorphosis stages. Some degree of continuity, if not even identity between yolk proteins and blood proteins, between one generation and the next, is therefore quite possible.

Small metabolites such as amino-acids and nucleotides may readily be shown to enter developing oocytes after injection of radioactively-labelled samples into the blood stream of the female (see Kemp and Hibbard, 1960; Pantelouris, 1958; Ficq, 1960). The subsequent distribution of these tracers in the various embryonic cells can then be followed by means of autoradiography (Bourne, 1952). This can be combined with biochemical separation methods, subsequently applied to the embryos that develop from these oocytes, provided that a long-lived isotope such as tritium (H3) or carbon (C14) is used. In such experiments the follicle cells become heavily labelled as well as the oocytes. It is not certain what special role they may play in the transport of metabolites into the oocyte. Electron microscope observations suggest strongly that some interchange of materials may occur, however: Hope, Humphries, and Bourne (1963) have described microvilli projecting into the surface of the follicle cells from the cortical layer of the oocyte in the newt, *Triturus viridescens*. The follicle cells, on their side, have large processes ('*macro*villi') indenting the surface of the oocytes (Fig. 3.4). It would be interesting to follow autoradiographically the rate and extent to which different-sized metabolites may pass through these villous surfaces.

Perhaps the most remarkable aspect of oocyte nutrition in amphibians is that it is so precisely controlled in relation to the breeding habits of the animal. There must be considerable adaptability in the rate of transfer of material, so that it becomes much less when the ovaries are regressing, in contrast to the large-scale 'bursts' of oocyte maturation in the breeding season. The onset of phases of intake of materials is presumably controlled by gonadotropic hormones. But, as yet, little is known of how these hormones govern biochemical events within the ovary and its germ cells in amphibians.

(b) The constitution of the oocyte

Amphibian oocytes contain, of course, reserve materials to supply the needs of the developing embryo (cf. Introduction, p. 3). The visible structures within these oocytes have been described repeatedly, with increasing finesse as the tools of observation have improved. The *egg* stages, but seldom the oocytes, have also been analysed biochemically in the past. Some of the older data listing total contents of protein, lipid, etc., have been superseded, however, and we shall refer here only to more recent analyses of cell components. First, in order to make clear the relationship between these components and their layout, some of the histological and cytochemical findings need brief consideration.

Hibbard (1928) gave a remarkably accurate and thorough description of oocyte structure in amphibians. More recently, Balinsky and Devis (1963) have described oogenesis in *Xenopus laevis* from electron microscope pictures, and Ward (1962) and Wartenberg (1962) have made similar studies of other species as well as *Xenopus*. Hope *et al.* (1964 *a* and *b*) have described oogenesis in the newt, *Triturus viridescens*. Since the overriding theme of these and other authors' recent work has been the mechanism and site of formation of yolk platelets, this topic will be considered first. It involves considering also whether or not pigment is synthesized in the same sites as yolk: a matter over which there has been some controversy.

(c) Formation of yolk platelets and pigment granules

Earlier accounts of yolk formation in oocytes describe it as taking place at the 'Balbiani nucleus' (Fig. 3.5 *a*), believed to be rich in mitochondria. Recent electron microscope studies have confirmed that this region consists largely of mitochondria (Fig. 3.5 *b*), clumped together with material which Balinsky and Devis (1963) interpret as a form of RNA. There is still considerable uncertainty as to whether or not the yolk platelets form directly from the mitochondria. Lanzavecchia (1960) believed that they do, and Balinsky and Devis (1963) described what they

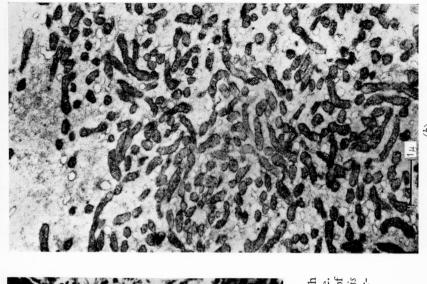

(b)

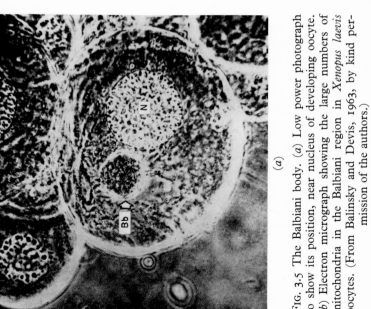

(a)

FIG. 3·5 The Balbiani body. (a) Low power photograph to show its position, near nucleus of developing oocyte. (b) Electron micrograph showing the large numbers of mitochondria in the Balbiani region in *Xenopus laevis* oocytes. (From Balinsky and Devis, 1963, by kind permission of the authors.)

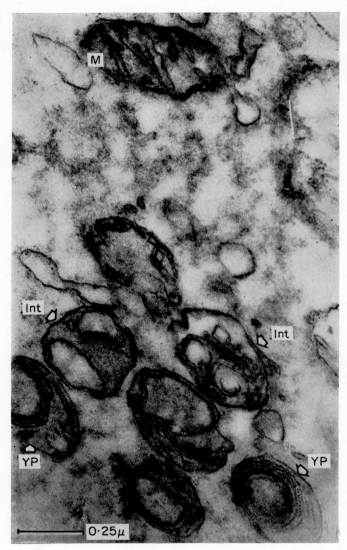

FIG. 3.6 (a) Transformation of mitochondria and of multivesicular bodies into yolk platelets, in *Xenopus laevis* (Balinsky and Devis, 1963). (a) Supposed stages in transformation of mitochondria into yolk precursors. (M) = mitochondrion; (Int) = partly transformed stage, with irregular internal membrane; (YP) = yolk platelet precursor.

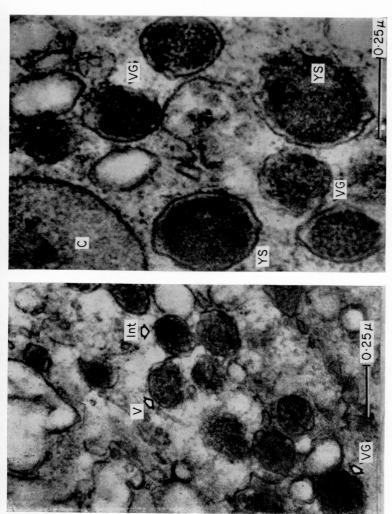

FIG. 3.6 (b) Supposed stages of secondary yolk formation from multivesicular bodies. (V) = typical multivesicular body; (Int) = intermediate stage; (VG) = coarsely granular body; (YS) = finely granular body (secondary peripheral yolk); (C) = a cortical granule.

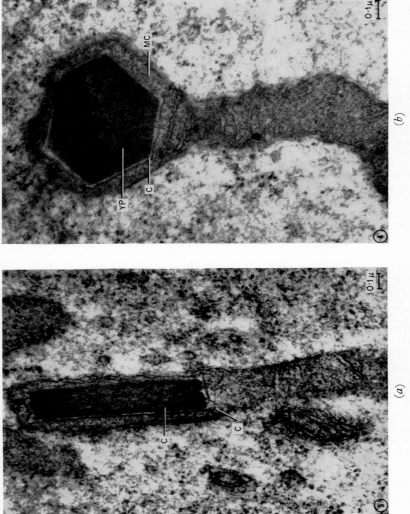

FIG. 3.7 (*a* and *b*) Yolk platelets apparently forming within mitochondria. (From Ward, 1962, by kind permission.) YP = yolk platelet; MC = mitochondrion; C = periphery of crystalline lattice.

claimed to be a series of intermediate stages of mitochondrion breakdown and yolk synthesis, in *Xenopus laevis* (Fig. 3.6 *a*). Hope *et al.*
(1964 *a*), on the other hand, have observed apparent yolk-formation in
membranous bodies (Fig. 3.6 *b*) which they considered might be transformed (or degenerate) mitochondria. Hope *et al.* were more reserved
in their interpretations of the reports of other investigators, notably of
Ward (1962) and of Wartenberg (1962), whose electron micrographs
show yolk platelets forming on the ends of mitochondria (Fig. 3.7 *a* and
b). They commented that at least in the oocytes of the larval gonads that
Ward examined, the yolk might well be a remnant from the embryonic
life of this larva. Yolk is known to persist for some time in the germ
cells of larvae before it is eventually broken down in the vicinity of
mitochondria. This means, of course, that there is some carry-over of
the previous generations's yolk into the new germ cells. It may be
assumed that at least some of the templates for the synthesis of new
yolk may be carried over too, particularly since RNA is believed to be a
constituent of the yolk.

The consensus of evidence makes it clear that mitochondria are closely
involved in yolk synthesis: but it is still a matter of doubt whether the
yolk is directly derived from them. In favour of this view, one may
point out that Ward's observations were made on adult frogs as well as
larvae, and that both he and Wartenberg have most carefully described
certain vesicles on the ends of mitochondria which they believe may be
sites of yolk synthesis. (It should be noted for general interest that the
structure and constitution of the egg yolk has been described much
more fully in birds (see Williams, 1965) than in amphibians. Bellairs
(1964) has reviewed this work and concludes that mitochondria are
probably indirectly involved in yolk synthesis, but that there is no evidence that yolk is actually synthesized *on* the mitochondria. It forms, in
fact, from vacuoles near the mitochondria.)

The functions of the many types of 'vesicles' seen in developing
amphibian oocytes are not yet fully elucidated and some of them, at
least, appear to form pigment. Wartenberg (loc. cit.) described the
formation of pigment granules in vesicles placed at the ends of mitochondria – similar to those described as forming yolk, by the authors
mentioned above. Balinsky and Devis observed pigment granules in
oocytes of *Xenopus*, in multivesiculate bodies which were again similar

D

to those that formed yolk. Hope *et al.* on the other hand describe the pigment as forming in 'membrane-limited vesicles' which they think are part of the Golgi apparatus (Fig. 3.8 *a–f*). But in *Xenopus*, Balinsky and Devis observed that the Golgi vesicles formed cortical granules, and not pigment. Fig. 3.9 summarizes the possibilities suggested by all these authors and gives a tentative suggestion as to how the somewhat conflicting interpretations may be resolved.

Although it may seem only to add to the confusion, it would not be fair to omit mentioning that more than one investigator (e.g. Hwan Sun Sung, 1962) has claimed that mitochondria form *from* yolk. This view has not gained general acceptance, but will be difficult either to refute or confirm conclusively from electron micrograph evidence alone.

(d) Sequence of sites of yolk platelet synthesis
There have been varying reports about the sequence of yolk synthesis and its transport within the developing oocyte. Wittek (1952) and Kemp (1956) claim that it first appears peripherally in the cortex, then extends inwards towards the centre of the cell. At later stages some yolk is formed in the perinuclear zone, at the time when there is a 'cap' of RNA over the nucleus (see below). Ornstein (1956) has noted signs of interaction between mitochondria and nucleoli at the nuclear membrane: it is well known, too, that the nucleoli are themselves capable of protein synthesis.

Both fluorescent antibody-labelling and radioactive tracer methods have been used in attempts to mark and trace the movements of the yolk materials in oocytes. Pantelouris (loc. cit. above) claimed on the basis of experiments with 35-S-methionine and 14-C-glycine, that materials passed first from cytoplasm to nucleus, then back to the cytoplasm, during yolk synthesis, suggesting an exchange of 'information' between nucleus and cytoplasm. Sentein (1963) has noted a similar sequence in the changing localizations of Periodic-acid–Schiff-positive material (mucopolysaccharide). But it is difficult to draw concise conclusions about the direction in which materials are moving, simply from autoradiographs and histochemical procedures. There is no evidence that the nucleus exerts any direct control over either the synthesis or the distribution of the yolk.

We still do not know how the eventual graded distribution of yolk

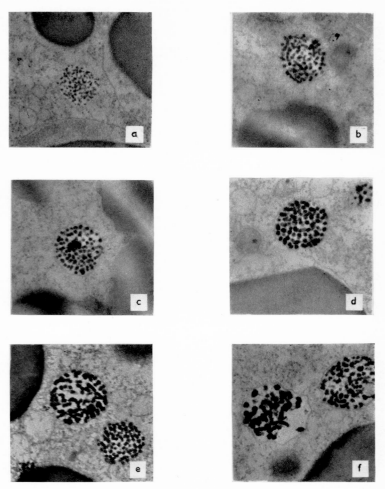

FIG. 3.8 Stages of pigment-formation within vesicles in oocytes of *Rana pipiens*. (From an original kindly supplied by J. Hope.) (*a*)–(*f*) Successive stages up to liberation of pigment granules.

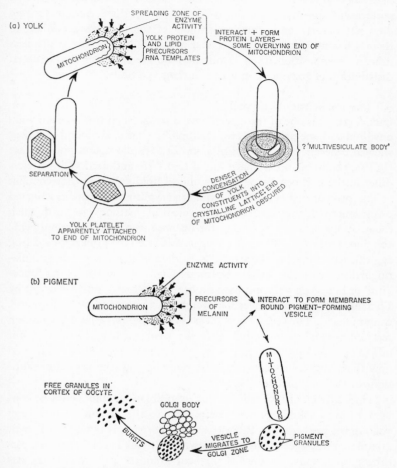

FIG. 3.9 Suggested interpretation of the various views on yolk and pigment synthesis. Mitochondria are supposed to *secrete* some of the enzymes responsible and, in the synthetic processes that follow, may be partially obscured by aggregating products which may *appear* to be an integral part of them.

platelets of different sizes from animal to vegetal pole is achieved. The pattern appears to be laid down during the synthesis period, for one does not observe any 'grand re-shuffle' of the platelets according to their different sizes at any later stage. If the different-sized platelets differ in composition, their layout may be the result of a differential distribution of enzymes concerned in their synthesis.

(e) The constituents of yolk

Panijel (1950) is one of those who have distinguished two types of yolk, one lipid and one proteinaceous, in amphibian eggs. He found that they showed differences in composition and in phosphoprotein phosphatase (PPPase) content: others have found that different-sized yolk platelets differ in the proportions of protein and of lipid yolk that they contain.

The protein components of amphibian yolk have been investigated using micro-electrophoretic and serological methods to distinguish them. Ringle and Gross (1962), for instance, recognized five antigenic components in the yolk of frogs' eggs. Wallace (1963 a) examined frog egg extracts similar to those already studied in hen's egg yolk, and distinguished two main classes of protein. One, (S), resembles the 'phosvitin' of hen's egg yolk and has also been recognized in the frog egg by Flickinger (1960); its molecular weight is 32,000 and its phosphorus content 8·4%. The second of Wallace's components (F) is a lipoprotein resembling the 'α-lipovitellin' of the hen's egg, with a molecular weight of 420,000. Its lipid content is 17·55%. Wallace (1963 b) has suggested how these two components may be built up into the crystalline subunits of the yolk platelet (Fig. 3.10).

Schjeide et al. (1955) claimed that amphibian 'vitellin' could be converted into a soluble protein comparable to the 'livetin' of hen's egg yolk, in the presence of a PPPase that was apparently bound to pigment granules. Flickinger (1956) also showed that yolk is solubilized in testtube preparations, so long as pigment granules are present. He has suggested that the solubilization of yolk in the embryo at later stages in its development occurs by a similar mechanism involving the pigment granules. This work needs repeating with purer preparations of the reacting components, however.

The crystalline lattice structure of yolk platelets is particularly well depicted in Karasaki's (1963 a), Ward's (1962), and Wischnitzer's (1957)

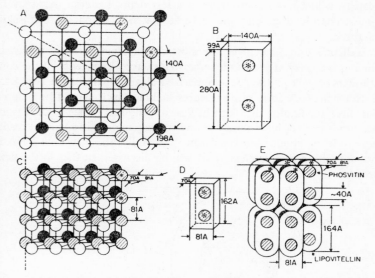

FIG. 3.10 Crystalline lattice structure of the yolk platelet. Models for the possible arrangements of yolk proteins within the main-body crystal, all drawn to the same scale. A, an arrangement of phosvitin molecules in a face-centred cubic lattice; the more darkly shaded molecules are in the background; the solid lines connect molecules which are 198 Å apart; when viewed from the orientation indicated by the dashed line, a regular hexagonal array of particles would appear to have an 81-Å centre-to-centre distance from one another; B, a structural unit from A (containing the two phosvitin molecules indicated by an asterisk and an unindicated lipovitellin molecule); C, an arrangement of phosvitin molecules indicated by a simple hexagonal lattice; the solid lines connect molecules which are 81 Å apart; when viewed from the orientation indicated by the dashed line, a hexagonal array of particles similar to the case in A would be observed; D, a structural unit from C; E, proposed model for the arrangement of structural units in the main-body crystal of the amphibian yolk platelet; a rhombohedral unit cell would be composed of four structural units (indicated by an asterisk); the phosvitin molecules are arranged in a simple hexagonal lattice. (From Wallace, 1963, by kind permission.)

43

electron micrographs. The lattice forms the dense, central part of the platelet while peripherally there is a less dense material that may be polysaccharide. Fig. 3.11 shows these materials in one of Karasaki's pictures.

Williams (1965) has given the most comprehensive recent review of the biochemistry of yolk. Our somewhat sketchy knowledge of the constituents of yolk platelets is summarized diagrammatically in Fig. 3.12. Two particularly interesting features included in it should be pointed out: first, the finding that both PPPase activity and protease (cathepsin) activity is present in or closely bound to the platelets, in apparent readiness to bring about their breakdown: secondly, the view that RNA is present within the platelets. This will be discussed further in the next section.

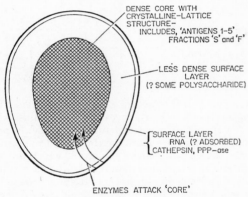

DENSE CORE WITH
CRYSTALLINE–LATTICE
STRUCTURE–
INCLUDES, 'ANTIGENS 1–5'
FRACTIONS 'S' and 'F'

LESS DENSE SURFACE
LAYER
(? SOME POLYSACCHARIDE)

SURFACE LAYER
RNA (? ADSORBED)
CATHEPSIN, PPP–ase

ENZYMES ATTACK 'CORE'

FIG. 3.12 Diagram illustrating the known facts about the composition of the yolk platelet.

(f) RNA in the developing oocyte

Analysis of the various forms of RNA, both ribosomal and non-particulate, can now be undertaken by means of density-gradient separation methods. These have already been used with some success by Brown and his collaborators, who have, in addition, been able to distinguish newly-synthesized RNA by 32P-labelling procedures. Brown and Littna (1964 *a* and *b*) followed the synthesis of ribosomal and of 'transfer' (soluble) RNA in oocytes and in embryonic stages of *Xenopus*

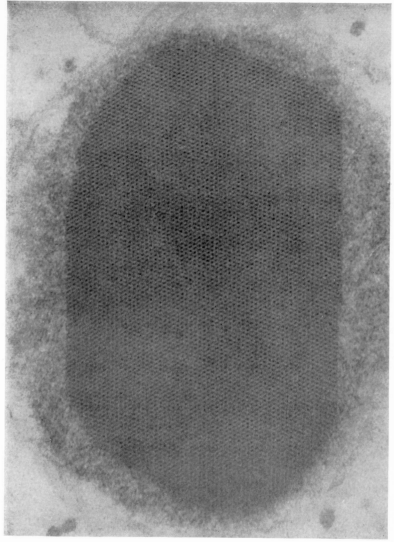

FIG. 3.11 Electron micrograph showing the dense, central crystalline lattice structure of the yolk platelet and the less dense outer zone. (From an original kindly supplied by S. Karasaki.)

laevis and found that there is more extensive synthesis of ribosomes in the oocyte than in the early embryo. They did not follow a series of oocyte stages but selected only the largest, mature ones. With these, however, they obtained very clear profiles of the kinds of RNA present: Fig. 3.13, taken from their paper, shows one of these. They have also succeeded in analysing the base composition of the ribosomal RNA of oocytes, finding that it is essentially similar to adult ribosomal RNA. Finamore and Volkin (1961), who emphasize the high proportion of 0·5M perchloric acid-soluble RNA in eggs as compared with adult cells, also carried out base analyses and found that the soluble RNA has more adenosine and uracil but less guanine and cytosine than the insoluble (ribosomal) RNA. In their base ratio analyses, Edström and Gall (1963)

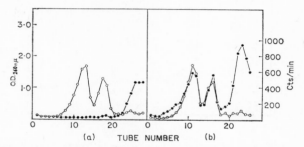

FIG. 3.13 Profile of the RNA constituents of oocytes of *Xenopus laevis*. (From Brown and Littna, 1964, by kind permission of the authors.)

found that the nucleolar RNA closely resembled cytoplasmic ribosomal RNA in base composition. They inferred from this that the nucleolar RNA might be a precursor of ribosomal RNA. Jones (1965) has made a similar suggestion, from electron microscope work on *Xenopus*.

It is possible by cytochemical methods to carry out a more complete study of the sites at which RNA synthesized – although this kind of study does not distinguish between the forms of RNA. Some of the earlier cytochemical findings are helpful, however. Kemp (1953) showed an animal-vegetal gradient in basophilia in the frog oocyte, and Wittek (1952) as well as Osawa and Hayashi (1952) observed a cap of RNA to one side of the nucleus at late oogenesis stages. The findings of these last two authors are summarized in Fig. 3.14. Another approach – that

of labelling with tritiated RNA precursors and then making autoradiographs – has been employed extensively by Ficq (1960). After injection
of H^3-cytidine into the female she found labelling first in the nucleus,
then later in a stable RNA of the cytoplasm, and eventually in a more
rapidly metabolized cytoplasmic RNA. It is not surprising to have
evidence of a nucleo-cytoplasmic interchange during RNA synthesis
(cf. the results of Pantelouris, 1958).

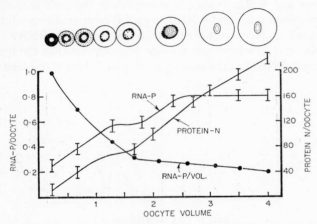

FIG. 3.14 Distribution and concentrations of RNA in the developing
oocyte of *Triturus pyrrhogaster*. (After Osawa and Hayashi, 1953.)

A number of authors have claimed that yolk platelets contain RNA.
Wallace (1963 *a* and *b*) contested this, however, after isolating yolk platelets of *Rana pipiens* in the presence of polyvinyl pyrrolidone (PVP) and
sucrose. He claimed that they were less damaged by this procedure than
by other extraction methods. It seems possible, however, that in his
case the RNA was not detectable simply because it remained closely
bound within the platelets instead of being liberated by damage. The
question whether or not RNA is an integral part of the yolk platelets'
internal structure must remain open at present.

Nucleolar RNA has become an object of intensive study recently. An
anucleolate mutant of *Xenopus* has been found to synthesize much less
RNA of the molecular weight typical of 'messenger RNA' than the

normal embryo (Brown and Gurdon, 1963). Sirlin (pers. comm. 1964) has evidence that nucleoli contain messenger RNA, from analyses of isolated nucleoli. Ozban, Tandler and Sirlin (1964) also noted recently a higher rate of methylation in nucleolar RNA than in other forms of RNA in oocytes of *Bufo*. This is interpreted as indicating that the nucleolus contains 'transfer RNA' (the form that attaches amino-acids to ribosomal templates during protein synthesis). Another recent observation on the nucleolus is that it contains, in many species, strands called 'nucleonemata'. Wischnitzer (1963) has described nucleonemata in oocytes. Their function is a matter of speculation so far – it seems likely that they could be sites for the synthesis of RNA templates. If so, these templates could then either be released into the nucleoplasm, or even used within the nucleolus since we know (Brandt and Finamore, 1963) that nucleoli can carry out protein synthesis: they take up amino-acids and have demonstrable amino-acid activating enzyme activity as well.

The origin of nucleoli in the egg and embryo of amphibians is not clear; Kemp (1956 *b*) suggested that they are formed on the loops of the 'lampbrush chromosomes' that are so characteristic of the amphibian oocyte. Macgregor (1965) doubts if this is literally true, though in one newt species 'nucleolar organisers' can be seen closely associated with the loops. It has recently been shown that the loops are sites of a highly organized RNA turnover, so they may synthesize protein too (Gall and Callan, 1962). In many amphibian species a new crop of nucleoli appears much later on, in the blastula stage, and early embryonic stages are characterized by a dearth of nucleoli. It is this synthesis at the blastula stage, as well as the RNA synthesis, that fails in the anucleolate mutant of *Xenopus*. This mutant provides a most interesting example of gene control over the production of a well-defined intracellular structure.

(g) DNA in the oocyte

The developing oocyte may be claimed as the first animal cell in which the presence and distribution of DNA was seriously questioned. The apparent anomalies observed led to discoveries that seemed quite revolutionary when they were made. First, there were reports that in oocytes of echinoderms, the germinal vesicle contained no DNA at all, at certain stages (Marshak and Marshak, 1954); later, in complete contrast, claims were put forward that not only the nucleus but also the cytoplasm contained stores of DNA-like material. Hoff-Jørgensen and Zeuthen first claimed this for enucleated cytoplasm of *Rana pipiens* oocytes in 1952. Their results were disbelieved by many at first, but have gradually gained acceptance. Recently, the presence of cytoplasmic DNA in oocytes and early embryos of the Salamander, *Pleurodeles waltlii*, has been confirmed by Baltus and Brachet (1962) using a new, fluorimetric method to identify DNA. This DNA is found in Feulgen-positive cytoplasmic bodies. Brachet and Ficq (1965), using ^{14}C-Actinomycin D as a marker, believe that some DNA may also be bound to the surfaces of the yolk platelets. There have been widely varying reports as to the quantity of DNA in the cytoplasm: all the figures given are equivalent to thousands of nuclei, however. As will be seen later, this DNA reserve gradually becomes used up, presumably by transfer to the nuclei, during embryonic development until, by the tailbud stage in *Rana* (Sze, 1953 *a*) and in *Xenopus* (Bristow and Deuchar, 1964), the concentration of DNA per cell is equal to that in adult cells.

The apparent absence of DNA from the germinal vesicle, which Marshak and Marshak (1954) reported (see above), has been found to be an illusion: the Feulgen stain appears negative at some stages of oocyte development (this is true in amphibians, too), possibly owing to dilution in the relatively large volume of nucleoplasm. The chromosomal DNA is also 'shrouded' to some extent by the broad loops, containing RNA, in their peculiar 'lampbrush' arrangement. The further significance of these loops is being investigated by Gall and Callan (see Macgregor, 1965).

(h) Soluble components of the cytoplasm

Most biochemical analyses of oocytes have been made on total homogenates, including yolk, so that they are difficult to interpret precisely. A little electrophoretic work has, however, been carried out on saline extracts that are yolk-free. Barth and Barth (1954) were the pioneers in such work, and they used potassium chloride extracts of *Rana pipiens* eggs. Since then, improved methods for small-scale electrophoresis have been developed. Using cellulose acetate strips, Denis (1961) was able to separate as many as eleven discrete protein bands in extracts

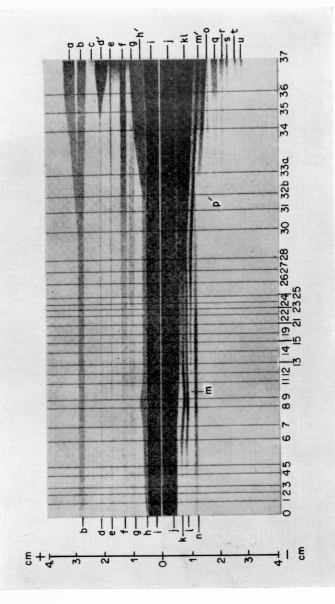

FIG. 3.15 Different protein bands identified in extracts of *Pleurodeles* embryos from fertilization to early tadpole stages. (From Denis, 1961, by kind permission of the author.) Figures represent stages of development; letters represent protein bands from electrophoresis.

from eggs and embryos of the salamander, *Pleurodeles waltlii* (Fig. 3.15). No one has successfully followed the protein pattern during oogenesis, however. Inoue (1961 *a* and *b*) attempted to do so, distinguishing a number of different proteins in embryo extracts by serological methods and also using specific chemicals to inhibit certain end-groups, in the hopes of being able to classify the proteins further. The extracts from oocytes showed very low titres of protein compared with the embryonic stages, but at least Inoue's data show that some of the serologically specific proteins present in the cytoplasm of embryos are already being synthesized in the oocyte.

It has also been possible to carry out micro-scale enzyme assays on oocytes and the best-known enzymes have all been found to be present. Weber and Boell (1955) showed that mitochondrial enzymes were active in the oocyte, and Petrucci (1960) observed a particularly high cytochrome oxidase activity during the phase of maximum vitellogenesis when, interestingly enough, the mitochondria lose their normal form. Boell (see loc. cit.) has also shown that glycolytic enzymes are present in the oocyte.

In some interesting preliminary work, Nace *et al.* (1960) found that there are at least four types of lactate dehydrogenase (LDH) present in the oocyte, just as there are in the adult. The exact relationship between the forms of LDH in the oocyte and those in the adult has not yet been elucidated: it will be very interesting to see how they differ and to what extent there is an 'embryogenesis' of LDH molecules, as has been found to be the case in mammal and chick embryos (Wiggert and Villee, 1964). Nace *et al.* (loc. cit.) have also had success with fluorescent antibody labelling of oocyte proteins and have noted slight changes in their intracellular distribution (although no different antigens appear) during and after ovulation.

Much less attention has been paid to soluble components of the oocyte other than proteins. This may be largely owing to the lack of sufficiently micro-methods for analysing the types within any major class of non-protein molecules. A few gross findings may be mentioned: *lipid* accumulates towards the vegetal pole region (a foreshadowing of the distribution of yolk platelets?) but the time at which this localization begins has not been noted. *PAS-positive material* (mucopolysaccharide) accumulates in the regions of platelet synthesis and also in the nucleus

(Sentein, 1963). Later it lies mainly to one side of the egg. The significance of this distribution is not understood. Analyses of *glycogen* show that there is more acid-soluble glycogen in ovarian oocytes than in those taken from the oviduct (Fitch and Merrick, 1958).

One of the reasons why so many of the above findings have to be quoted without qualification or comment, is our ignorance of the metabolism of these early stages, since, like the embryos of mammals, they are inaccessible *in vivo*.

(i) Components of the egg cortex

Attention has been focused on the cortex in recent years, since grafting experiments (Curtis, 1960, 1962) have shown that after fertilization the cortical material in the region of the grey crescent acquires 'information' essential to future development, and somehow transmits this to other parts of the embryo. The ultrastructure and biochemistry of the cortex need much further study. Wartenberg and Schmidt (1961) have looked at its ultrastructure in *Rana pipiens*, noting particularly the presence of polysaccharide granules: these are not, however, present in the Urodele, *Triturus alpestris*. Balinsky and Devis (loc. cit.) have observed with the electron microscope some of the changes that occur at fertilization, and Dollander (1956) also studied the cortex in amphibian eggs by electron microscopy (see next section). Biochemical studies have shown, so far, only that the PPPase activity of the grey crescent is higher than in other cortical regions (Nass, 1962) and that it is particularly susceptible to trypsin and chymotrypsin digestion (Rosenbaum, 1958).

(j) Changes that occur at fertilization

Most of the work on metabolic changes at fertilization has been carried out on sea-urchin eggs which are easy to fertilize artificially. For further information about these events in echinoderms, the reader is referred to Monroy (1965).

One of the events that has been described very fully in echinoderms and is therefore taken as exemplary of 'what to look out for' in other forms, is the change in the cortical granules. These, in sea-urchins (a beautifully transparent material) appear to burst and then to form the 'fertilization membrane' which rises off the egg (Balinsky, 1960 *a*). The fluid between this membrane and the egg – in the perivitelline space – is

thought in some cases to be a product of the cortical granules. Wartenberg and Schmidt (loc. cit.) observed that polysaccharide material was
discharged from the cortical granules of *Rana pipiens* into the perivitelline space at fertilization. The observations of Balinsky and Devis
(loc. cit.) also indicate that in oocytes of *Xenopus* the cortical granules
undergo changes similar to those described in the sea-urchin. Pasteels
(1961), reviewing events in amphibians, pointed out that there is a
fundamental difference between Anurans and Urodeles. In Anurans,
events seem to follow the sea-urchin pattern, although slowly (the

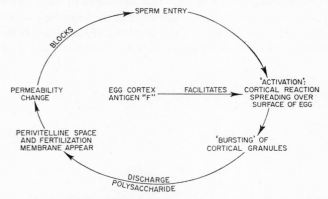

FIG. 3.16 Diagrammatic summary of the events taking place
at fertilization.

fertilization membrane taking at least 10 min. to rise). In Urodeles,
however, there is already a perivitelline space in the mature oocyte.
This basic difference may be related to the fact that fertilization
normally takes place internally in Urodeles, whereas it is external in
the Anura.

Nace and Lavin (1964) believe that the antigen 'F' which they found
in the egg cortex of *Rana pipiens* may be essential to fertilization, since
'anti-F' antibody preparations prevent both activation and development
in a high percentage of cases.

Virtually nothing is known, still, about the chemical changes that are
brought about by the entry of the sperm into the amphibian egg. None
of them can be essential to very early development, for cleavages take

place normally in parthenogenetic and hybrid embryos, although development eventually becomes arrested before gastrulation. Løvtrup (1962) has followed the changes in permeability in different regions of the egg cortex during fertilization, but observed no lasting difference in the dorsal region or in any other region related to the point of entry of the sperm. From a number of artificial activation experiments it has become clear that only the 'cortical reaction' (see Chapter Two), which needs no more than a needle-prick to set it off, is necessary to initiate cleavage. It is not until the late blastula stage (significantly, the time when new nucleoli should appear) that development stops or becomes abnormal if a normal sperm has not entered the secondary oocyte.

To conclude this account, a brief summary of the events believed to be significant in the fertilization process has been given in Fig. 3.16.

CHAPTER FOUR

The Earliest Phases of Development: Cleavage and the Formation of the Blastula

Cleavage is, in amphibians, the phase of development about which we know least, partly because it is amenable only to the few kinds of experiment that do not damage large proportions of the embryo too drastically. Another difficulty in experimentation on cleavage stages is the time factor: before one is ready to carry out the procedure on it, a two-cell stage may have become a four-cell stage, and the problem of ensuring uniformity within any batch of embryos being collected for analysis is very great. Consequently, by far the majority of experiments are carried out on later, gastrula and neurula stages. These have the additional attraction that the future organs and tissues are by then recognizable, and they are undergoing particularly interesting morphogenetic movements as well as critical stages of cell-differentiation.

This is not to say, however, that there are no special processes occurring during cleavage besides the cell divisions that result simply from mitotic divisions of the nucleus. Indeed, cleavage can take place in the total absence of the nucleus, providing the egg has been suitably 'activated' by some treatment such as pricking it. As has been emphasized already (Chapter Two), the cleavage follows a highly organized pattern. Since development can proceed normally after experimental derangement of this pattern, however, any rigid organization must be considered 'unnecessary'. Nevertheless, a co-ordinating mechanism normally exists and it normally determines very exactly the timing and orientation of every cell division in the early embryo. Recollecting the relatively large size of amphibian eggs, it is clear that this co-ordinating mechanism must be capable of acting over long distances (i.e. milli-metres) – either on the surface of the embryo or across its internal diameter. According to experimental evidence, control of cleavage probably operates at the surface of the embryo, in the cortex. Changes in the cortex appear to initiate furrow-formation and the eventual divisions between the cells. So we shall first give some attention to what is known and has been speculated about the mechanism of furrow-formation during cleavage.

(a) The mechanism of cleavage

As with the investigation of so many mechanisms in biology, information tends to have been obtained from only a limited number of forms that happen to have been found convenient for laboratory work. Studies on cleavage have been made with the greatest success on echinoderm embryos, and it has to be remembered that the general theories arising from such work do not necessarily apply to any other animal group. Much of the recent work on sea-urchins has been carried out by Swann and Mitchison, who have reviewed the subject fully (1958). Selman and Waddington (1955) have described rather different findings in amphibians. Some of the biochemical implications of these and their differences from echinoderms will be considered here.

The earlier theories as to the mechanism of cleavage remained plausible only so long as ignorance of the structure and biochemical composition of the egg prevented their refutation. Thus, the simple 'surface tension theory' of Spek (see Swann and Mitchison's review) assumed that the egg behaved like a liquid sphere. This naturally fell into disrepute as soon as the cortex was shown to have the properties of an elastic solid. Swann and Mitchison's 'expanding membrane' theory by which they attempted to explain the onset of cleavage in sea-urchin eggs stressed just these elastic properties. But in doing so, it failed to account for the apparently non-elastic behaviour at the furrow itself, where the cortex seems to buckle inwards passively. Another important aspect of Swann and Mitchison's theory, which has some evidence to support it, is that the cortex transmits a surface change at fertilization. Under polarized light, Rothschild and Swann (1949) observed a wave of birefringence spreading over the egg surface from the point of sperm entry. This kind of change is in accord with bimolecular leaflet theories of the structure of membranes, according to which there are two layers of folded protein molecules, with a negative intrinsic birefringence

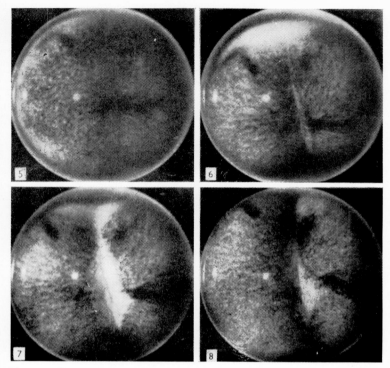

FIG. 4.1 Photographs of the upper surface of the newt's egg as the first cleavage furrow forms, taken by time-lapse cinematography. (From Selman and Waddington, 1955, by kind permission of the authors.)

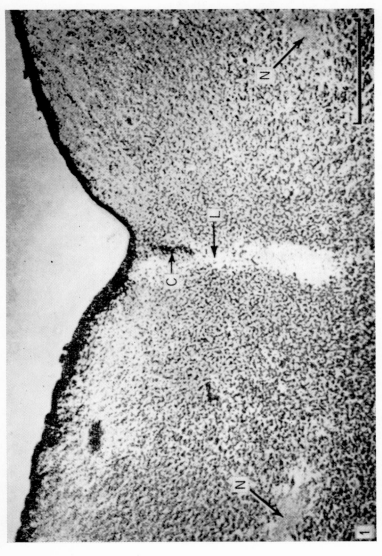

FIG. 4.2 Section through furrow region of newt's egg, showing submerged cortex (C) continuous with lamellar precursor (L) of new cell membrane. N = nucleus. (From Selman and Waddington, 1955.) Scale in R.H. bottom corner indicates 100μ.

owing to the radial orientation of the folded segments, and between these layers are radially oriented lipid layers. A positive form bire-fringence results when the protein layers unfold and expand into a tangential orientation.

Swann and Mitchison's polarized light observations could not, un-fortunately, be made in the region of the cleavage furrow itself. Selman and Waddington (1955) using newts' eggs, concentrated particularly on events in this furrow region. They showed that new cortical material is synthesized here and that the furrow is a most active region during cleavage. Using the viscometer designed by Swann and Mitchison, Selman and Waddington showed that just before the furrow forms, there is maximum rigidity at the surface, then at the moment of furrow-formation, at each cleavage, the surface rigidity falls. The result of this cycle of surface changes is that the embryo (which, after removal of its jelly and vitelline membrane, tends to flatten to a bun-shape) assumes a more rigid spherical shape just before each cleavage. The furrow which then forms extends inwards only at first, out of sight of the surface, but immediately after this the embryo appears to 'relax', flattening again and allowing the new cleavage furrow to gape, exposing a white, un-pigmented area of newly synthesized cortex (Fig. 4.1). This new cortex is seen in histological sections to be continuous with the lamella that is laid down as a precursor of the new cell membrane, at the site of the former metaphase plate (Fig. 4.2).

The immediate, obvious problem posed by Waddington and Selman's work is that of *how* new cortex is synthesized. Unfortunately, we have no means of measuring the localization of enzyme activities or of tracer uptake in the regions of synthesis. It would be very difficult to do this precisely since the time intervals of individual cleavages are very short. The possibility of slowing down cleavage with mitotic inhibitors has been entertained, but most agents used (see Sentein, 1961, 1964) derange the nuclear spindle and so would probably produce abnormalities in the synthesis of cortical material and of the cell membrane too. The earliest cleavages in amphibians are also impossible to arrest by lowering the temperature within physiological limits; energy reserves appear to continue to be mobilized regardless of external temperature, at this stage.

Zotin (1964) has described the 'diastema' that forms at the site of the
E

former metaphase plate in the axolotl and, from experiments in which embryos were compressed so that the nuclear spindle lay at different angles in relation to this plate, concludes that the diastema *induces* furrow-formation. It should, however, be re-emphasized that cleavage can occur in the absence of nuclei. Briggs, Green, and King (1951) were the first to show in amphibians that after removal of the egg nucleus with a needle, cytoplasmic divisions nevertheless occurred and cell membranes formed, producing something very like a blastula apart

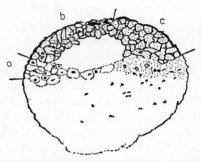

FIG. 4.3 Blastula-formation in the absence of a nucleus.
(From Waddington, 1956. *Principles of Embryology*.)

from the absence of nuclei (Fig. 4.3). Hence, all previous theories that have invoked some interaction between nucleus and cortex to account for the initiation of cleavage, must be discredited. Dan and Kujiyama (1963) have recently demonstrated the independence of the furrow movement in amphibian embryos. They fully corroborate Selman and Waddington's findings that there is a subcortical synthesis of material that later becomes the new cortex. In further discussion they also point out that this synthesis must take place *before* the furrow forms and independently of the nucleus since it is not prevented by inserting cellophane between the nucleus and the surface (a repeat of the experiment carried out by Waddington in 1952).

From the timing of events that Dan and Kujiyama suggest, it seems that the elucidation of the mechanisms initiating cleavage in amphibian eggs should be achievable by further biochemical study of this subcortical zone in the furrow.

(b) Energy utilization and requirements during cleavage

It has been shown (Brachet, 1935) that amphibian eggs can undergo the whole of the cleavage process, up to the early blastula stage, in complete anaerobiosis. They can also do so in the presence of cyanide, which blocks cytochrome oxidase activity. They are, however, dependent on an adequate reserve of ATP, as stressed by Barth and Jaeger (1947) and later by Brachet (1960). Below a certain critical level of ATP, cleavage is arrested. Agents which deplete the ATP store, or block its utilization, are therefore inhibitors of cleavage. Such an agent is dinitrophenol (Brachet, 1954) which uncouples oxidative and phosphorylative processes in the cell and therefore seriously impedes the resynthesis of ATP. Cleavage may also be blocked by a variety of other agents, however: some probably by virtue of their inhibition of RNA synthesis. Other agents, like chloroacetophenone (Sentein, 1961) and parachloromercuribenzoic acid (Barth, 1956) inactivate sulfhydryl (–SH) groups. Rapkine (1931) first stressed that the cell divisions are dependent on the formation of fibrillar proteins (such as those of the nuclear spindle) and that these fibrillar proteins contain sulphur which forms disulphide linkages. On denaturation, these liberate –SH groups. But it is not clear why the inactivation of –SH groups should in itself be inhibitory to cleavage.

For accounts of further work on cleavage inhibitors, the reader is referred to the work of Sentein (1964) and of Tencer (1961). Most of the effects have been a complete blockage of the process of mitosis: these treatments have not, therefore, facilitated in any way the study of processes that normally occur during cleavage.

One of the few observations on normal oxidative events during cleavage is that of Zeuthen (1955). He noted in a number of different eggs, including those of amphibians, a cyclic level of oxygen consumption, highest at prophase and lowest at telophase – beginning to *in*crease, surprisingly, during the so-called 'resting phase' or interphase. To follow the possible further significance of these cycles it is necessary to know more about cycles of DNA synthesis in the nucleus, as well as its concentration in the cytoplasm, during cleavage.

(c) The problem of DNA synthesis during cleavage

As remarked in the previous chapter, it is now established that the cytoplasm of the amphibian egg contains vast reserves of DNA. Hoff-

Jørgensen and Zeuthen (1952) suggest that the DNA content of the egg cytoplasm is equivalent to that of 5,000 haploid nuclei, in the frog *Rana platyrrhina*. This means that there is sufficient DNA reserve to supply all the new nuclei up to the early blastula stage. In agreement with the supposition that this DNA reserve *is* used by the nuclei, many authors have found that there is little or no increase of the total DNA per embryo until the blastula stage and that the concentration of DNA per cell, starting at a high figure, gradually falls until, by the tailbud stage in *Rana pipiens* (Sze, 1953 *a*) and in *Xenopus laevis* (Bristow and Deuchar, 1964) there is the same concentration of DNA per cell as in adult cells. There is some disagreement as to when the first increase in total DNA per embryo begins, however: Hoff-Jørgensen and Zeuthen, and Sze (loc. cit.) found constant values up to early gastrulation in *Triturus palmatus*. But Grant (1959) whose data were more precisely quoted, observed slight DNA increases much earlier – during cleavage – in *Rana pipiens*, and Bristow and Deuchar (loc. cit.) also noted a slight upward trend in DNA per embryo from cleavage stages onwards, in *Xenopus*. (See Grant, 1965, for a full review of nucleic acid synthesis in embryos.)

Taken as a whole, all of the measurements of DNA agree in indicating that during cleavage its rate of doubling is far below the rate of cell multiplication. Hence, since the nuclear content of DNA must remain constant, it is clear that some of the cytoplasmic reserve must be transferred to the nucleus at each division. But whether it is transferred after breakdown to constituent nucleotides, or as a high-molecular-weight precursor, is not known so far. It is possible to trace tritium-labelled nucleotides from the cytoplasm into the nuclei: this has been done autoradiographically with success by Moore (1959). But whether the thymidine enters as such, or bound in a larger molecule, is not ascertainable by this method.

One should, perhaps, stress that it is no departure from the current template hypotheses of DNA synthesis, to suggest that its precursors may exist as small molecules in the cytoplasm first. The DNA molecule is believed to be built up from smaller units in the presence of a suitable polymerase. We have no precise information yet about the localization of DNA polymerase in amphibian embryos. It is, on the other hand, well established that both RNAase and DNAase are abundantly present (Finamore, 1955; Coleman, 1962). According to Finamore there is a steady rise in RNAase activity and at the same time a decline in DNAase activity, during cleavage. Since both these enzymes are present all the time, it is reasonable to postulate that a continuous supply of nucleotide precursors is made available by DNA and RNA breakdown in the cytoplasm. Grant (1959) attempted with phosphorus-32 labelling to follow the sources of RNA and DNA in the developing embryo. He assumed, however, that the RNA level is constant during early development and that uptake of label into RNA was therefore an indication only of turnover rate. He found particularly high 'turnover' of RNA, on this argument. His results were complicated, however, by his use of two different methods of injecting tracer: both into the female and into the laid eggs. Recent evidence (Deuchar and Bristow, 1964) suggests that there is a steady, slow synthesis of RNA from the beginning of development. It seems most desirable to repeat this work, besides using more specific DNA and RNA precursors such as labelled nucleotides. In the meantime, 32P labelling and density gradient analysis of RNA from cleavage stages of *Xenopus laevis* (Brown and Littna, 1964 *a*) suggests that there is a marked synthesis of '4S', or 'messenger', RNA at this stage (see Fig. 10.13). In the salamander, *Pleurodeles*, cleavage is not prevented when *m*-RNA synthesis is blocked by actinomycin D, however (Brachet *et al.*, 1965).

There is plenty of evidence that cytoplasmic inhibitors have an effect on nuclei: Grant (1960) showed that treatment of egg cytoplasm with nitrogen mustard (which might be expected to derange the DNA configuration) had a deleterious effect also on nuclei transplanted into it. Moore (1960) showed in his pioneer 'back transfer' experiments (Fig. 4.4 *a*) that nuclei could no longer support normal development when returned to their own egg cytoplasm after having been transferred and having undergone a few divisions in a foreign egg cytoplasm. His findings have since been confirmed by Hennen (1963) using diploid nuclei which gave higher percentages of normal development (see Fig. 4.4 *b*). This is in contrast to a nucleus which has not been transferred to foreign cytoplasm: in the normal way even blastula and gastrula cell nuclei of the same species are capable of substituting for the zygote nucleus, as the brilliant nuclear transfer work by Briggs and King, and Gurdon (see Gurdon's review, 1964), has clearly shown. It is possible that the source of the nuclear abnormality in foreign cytoplasm is some incompatibility between the cytoplasmic DNA precursors and the kind of DNA in the nucleus. Hennen (1963) has observed that the nuclei undergo chromosomal alterations in foreign cytoplasm.

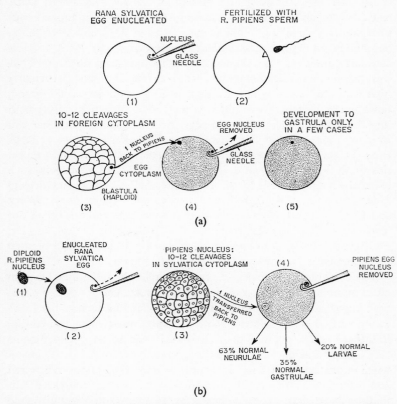

FIG. 4.4 'Back transfer' of nuclei between the two frog species, *Rana pipiens* and *Rana sylvatica*. (*a*) Moore's experiment using the haploid egg nucleus; (*b*) Hennen's transfers of diploid nuclei.

(d) The problem of cell differentiation during cleavage

Although cell differentiation occurs more obviously at gastrula and neurula stages, it is natural to look for the initiation of this process earlier still, during cleavage. The question as to how far the cleavage nuclei remain equivalent has interested embryologists ever since Spemann showed by his ligaturing experiment (Fig. 4.5 *a*) that each of the first two blastomeres was capable of forming a whole embryo. He

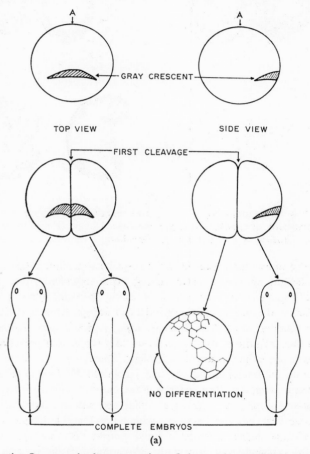

FIG. 4.5 (*a*) Spemann's demonstration of the equipotentiality of the first two blastomeres of the amphibian egg, provided that each contains part of the grey crescent. (Diagram from Barth, 1953, *Embryology*, by kind permission.)

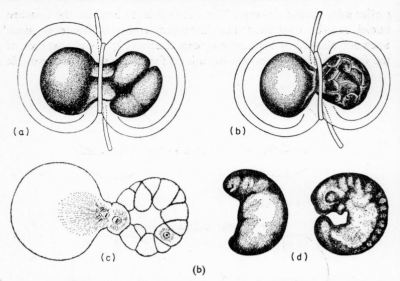

(b)

FIG. 4.5 (*b*) Spemann's 'loosened ligature' experiment, demonstrating the equipotentiality of cleavage nuclei at the 16-cell stage. (Photo from Raven, 1954, 'Outline of Developmental Physiology,' by kind permission.)

went on to show that a nucleus of the 16-cell stage, allowed to cross into non-nucleated cytoplasm after having been separated from it by a ligature (Fig. 4.5 *b*) was also capable of setting off normal development of a complete embryo. His and the evidence of Briggs, King, and Gurdon's nuclear transfer work (see Gurdon, 1964) make it now necessary to assume that cell-differentiation at these early stages is a property of the cytoplasm, since the nuclei are equivalent. The cytoplasm may, perhaps, act back on the nuclei in the way that Jacob and Monod (1961) suggest for enzyme induction (the scheme is set out in general terms in Fig. 4.6). Moore (1963) and Brachet (1964) are among those who have speculated that nuclear histones, which are readily detectable from early cleavage stages onwards in *Rana pipiens*, may function as gene-inactivators during early embryonic development. It has become popular, too, to think of gene activity being 'switched on' or 'switched off' by influences from the cytoplasm: but this must be recognized for what it is worth: a convenient idea and not in any way established fact.

Looking for possible cytoplasmic differences in the cleavage cells, one immediately notes the uneven distribution of yolk, pigment, and mitochondria. This results from their differential distribution in the egg, already described (p. 10). Since some, at least, of the visible structures carry specialized enzyme activities, this means a differential distribution of potential metabolic processes, too. The yolk platelets,

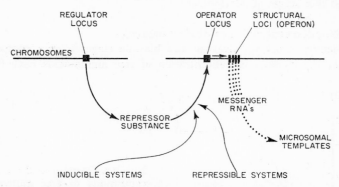

FIG. 4.6 Possible actions of the cytoplasm to modify gene function. (Reproduction of Jacob and Monod's scheme from Waddington, 1962, *New Patterns in Genetics and Development*)

for instance, appear to carry some phosphoprotein phosphatase activity as well as cathepsin activity (Harris, 1946; Deuchar, 1958 b). The pigment also may contain PPPase activity (Flickinger, 1956). Unfortunately, very little work has been done on the distribution of biochemical constituents in different cells at cleavage stages. The difficulty of dissecting different parts of the embryo for separate analysis, without damage to them, is too great. Even in physiological studies which are less exacting it has not been possible to show up differences between cleavage cells with any certainty. Once gastrulation has started, however (cf. Chapter Five), a higher metabolic activity is recognizable in the dorsal lip region. Løvtrup and Pigon (1958) have claimed that the position of the dorsal lip may be modified by differential exposure of its surface to oxygen, and Løvtrup (1965) argues that oxygen consumption may increase in this region prior to the formation of the dorsal lip.

It has to be admitted that very little work indeed has been done on the regional differences, either ultrastructural or biochemical, between different cells of the cleaving embryo. Butschak's is the chief electron microscope work (1960) that particularly refers to this stage. Weber and Boell (1962) have noted some regional differences in the properties of mitochondria, but their main interest, like that of other workers, was in the later stages of development.

(e) Biochemical changes during cleavage

Biochemical work on cleavage and blastula stages is very sparse: a few of the changes in concentration of free amino-acids have been

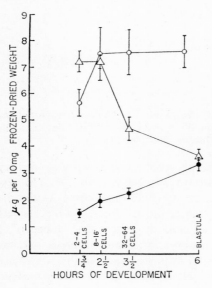

FIG. 4.7 Changes in the concentrations of free glutamic acid, aspartic acid and glutamine during cleavage in *Xenopus laevis*. Vertical lines indicate ± 1 standard error of the mean. $\bigcirc$ = glutamic acid; $\triangle$ = aspartic acid; $\bullet$ = glutamine.

followed (Deuchar, 1958 *a*) and show that glutamic acid and glutamine increase while aspartic acid decreases in concentration (Fig. 4.7). Possibly the first two are mobilized by the breakdown of protein reserves, to provide other amino-acid precursors by transamination. Aspartic acid, on the other hand, may suffer early depletion during nucleic acid synthesis.

The proteins of cleavage and blastula stages have been studied electrophoretically by Denis (1961), who distinguished eleven molecular species by this means, two of which appeared during cleavage (Fig. 3.15). Inoue (1961 *a* and *b*) made an extensive study of the antigens present at these stages in the newt, *Triturus pyrrhogaster*, finding that faster-moving components predominated at first, then slower-moving components (presumably larger molecules) appeared later. There was an overall increase in the quantities of antigens detectable during cleavage, and at the same time a decrease in the proportion of –SS– groups. It would be interesting to know if –SH groups *increase* correspondingly, in view of their possible implication in the cleavage mechanism (see above, p. 57).

The inconclusiveness of many of the findings reported in this chapter may be frustrating, but it is also both necessary and appropriate. Trends of events at the biochemical level cannot become clear or meaningful except by following them farther, to the stages at which different tissue and organ primordia become visibly distinct and may have distinct biochemical properties too. We have, however, experienced here a significant foretaste of the main problems: among them the central one of the biochemical basis of cell differentiation and the roles that DNA of both nucleus and cytoplasm, as well as other cytoplasmic components, may play in this process.

CHAPTER FIVE

Regional Biochemical Differences in the Early Gastrula

As soon as the first signs of the dorsal lip, where dorsal mesoderm invaginates, appear on the external surface of the embryo, the future topography of its tissues is immediately clear from detailed maps already compiled using the dorsal lip as reference point (cf. Chapter Two). For the biochemist, primary interest at once focuses on possible differences between these regions, connected with their future divergence in function and metabolism. With increasing refinements of the means of analysis, increasingly detailed differences are detectable, but our knowledge is still very limited.

Two main angles of approach have been used in the study of regional differences: the histological or cytological one in which the parts of the embryo are looked at *in situ* in microscopic sections, and biochemical procedures carried out on homogenates of tissues that have first been isolated by dissection. Both procedures have advantages and disadvantages. The histochemical methods, if handled with care, allow precise localization of materials, but they are seldom reliably quantitative. The biochemical methods are more suitable for accurate quantitative measurements, but they do not give a true picture of events in the intact cell. Ideally, both approaches should be utilized in all investigations and the results compared critically.

Most investigators of regional differences in the gastrula have been motivated by an urge to discover what special properties of the dorsal lip tissue may be responsible for its remarkable 'organizer' characteristics (Chapter Seven, p. 98), revealed in Spemann and Mangold's classical grafting experiments. This overriding interest in the 'organizer' and in the nature of neural induction has, in fact, biased the observations of amphibian embryologists so far as to blind them, in some instances, to properties of other gastrula regions that may be of equal importance in determining the course of future development. A certain 'mythology' has tended to be woven round the dorsal lip, some of which has since been proved erroneous. It is important, therefore, to consider all regional comparisons most critically. The possibility of discrepancies between *in situ* observations and those made on isolated pieces of tissue must also be borne in mind. Morphological studies have clearly shown that the differentiation of tissue isolates is often modified so that they form a wider range of structures than they would if left *in situ*. Since any modification of this kind must also involve biochemical changes, it is possible that some of the biochemical properties of isolates may be far removed from the properties of the tissues *in situ* during normal development.

It is not easy to establish the existence of regional biochemical differences in an embryo. Data must, of course, be adequate for statistical analysis, and this is often hard to achieve with the small samples of material available. In addition to this general difficulty, certain special difficulties arise in quantitative observations on amphibian embryos. For instance, if data are expressed 'per unit dry weight' or (as is also usual for biochemical measurements) 'per unit total nitrogen', there will be enormous differences in this base line in different regions of the embryo, owing to their different yolk content. The yolk, which is by far the heaviest and the richest nitrogenous component of amphibian embryos, is much more abundant in ventral than in dorsal regions. As an inevitable result of this unequal yolk distribution, data often suggest 'inferior' properties (as regards enzyme activities, respiration rate, etc.) in the ventral parts, when dry weight or total nitrogen are used as bases of reference. But in at least one instance (Deuchar, 1958 *b*) results have turned out in quite the opposite sense when expressed in another way – per cell, for example (see p. 73). It should be pointed out, too, that owing to the large and unequal quantities of the DNA-like material that is present in the cytoplasm, the DNA content cannot be used as an estimate of the number of cells, but actual cell counts have to be made.

Different but equally important sources of misinterpretation crop up in histochemical work. Surfaces that adsorb a dye will produce the optical illusion of dark colour wherever they are closely, rather than

68   BIOCHEMICAL ASPECTS OF AMPHIBIAN DEVELOPMENT

sparsely, spaced. The observer's eye also tends to summate the quantities of dye visible at several levels of focus. So the dorsal cells of the gastrula, which are smaller and therefore have more closely spaced membranes than the ventral cells, are likely to appear more densely stained than ventral ones, whatever the histochemical stain used. The only way in which the ventral cells may have an 'advantage' over dorsal ones in apparent affinity for dyes is by virtue of their higher yolk content: yolk platelets frequently adsorb dyes and thus obscure other specific localizations that may exist in the cytoplasm.

Because of these difficulties, every observation of regional differences in amphibian embryos that has so far been made creates further problems. Some of the outstanding findings will be reviewed briefly here. For more extensive discussions of regional differences in vertebrate eggs and early embryos, the reader is referred to Dalcq's account (1960), and to another review (Deuchar, 1965).

(a) Regional differences in carbohydrate metabolism

Glycogen, which is broken down to a small extent by anaerobic glycolysis in pre-gastrula stages, begins to disappear at a suddenly much higher rate in the blastula and gastrula (Boell, 1955). This phenomenon was observed histochemically by Woerdeman (1933) who noted particularly the rapid disappearance of glycogen from cells of the dorsal lip at the time of their invagination. Jaeger (1945) pointed out later that there was also a disappearance of glycogen in ventral lip cells as they invaginated, so that this was no special feature of the 'organizer' region and did not (as some had been inclined to argue) indicate that glycogen was the substance responsible for neural induction. It has since emerged from quantitative studies, however (see Brachet, 1960) that glycogen utilization is more rapid in the dorsal lip than in other regions of the gastrula. It is not surprising that the energy consumption of dorsal lip cells should exceed that of other regions at the time when these cells are undergoing active invagination movements.

There have been a number of studies of oxygen consumption in different regions – some of which were mentioned in the last chapter. Some time ago, Brachet (1934) observed a particularly high oxygen consumption in the dorsal lip of the early gastrula, but the more recent studies of Barth and Sze (1951) and of Sze (1953 b) on isolated pieces of gastrulae indicate highest values in the dorsal ectoderm. The neural ectoderm's oxygen consumption increases further after neural induction. There appear to be two gradients of oxygen consumption at the gastrula stage: an animal-vegetal and a dorso-ventral one. Experiments with vital dyes give the same picture. Brachet (1960) gives further details of these gradients.

(b) Regional differences in RNA at the gastrula stage

The study of RNA in differentiating cells has assumed a new significance since the 'messenger RNA' concept was formulated. If proteins are specified by 'messenger' RNA that copies the sequence of bases in nuclear DNA, it becomes of primary importance now to study the small quantities of 'messenger' that should appear when tissue-specific proteins are being synthesized. In fact, analyses of the different forms of RNA in amphibian embryos are already under way (e.g. Brown and Littna, 1964). They have so far worked only on whole embryos and oocytes. Waddington and Perkowska (1965) have, however, obtained preliminary evidence of regional differences in the types of RNA synthesized, in newt embryos.

The groundwork that established the importance of RNA for protein synthesis in embryonic development was to a large extent carried out by Brachet and his collaborators. He has described it more fully in his books (1957, 1960), and only a brief criticism of some of the interpretations that have been placed on his findings will be given here. In Brachet's earlier work, RNA was identified and measured by a non-specific staining procedure, using the basic dye, toluidine blue. Control staining reactions were carried out on preparations pre-treated with RNAase, which were shown to lose some of their basophilia. Nevertheless, there arose the danger of accepting 'basophilia' as synonymous with 'RNA'. Attempts were also made to judge the results quantitatively, by the intensity of the toluidine blue colour. It was concluded that the colour intensity was highest in the dorsal lip cells of the early gastrula, then later in the invaginated dorsal mesoderm. Some of the illustrations of these differences in staining intensity were not very convincing, however (Fig. 5.1). In subsequent work the methylgreen-pyronin stain was used to distinguish DNA and RNA. This stain has a much higher specificity than toluidine blue, and by means of it the distribution of RNA has been studied in some detail. Relative *concentrations* of RNA are not so easy to estimate, however, and we must await confirmation of Brachet's earlier results by improved methods before assuming that the RNA content is necessarily highest in the dorsal lip or archenteron roof as Brachet originally stated.

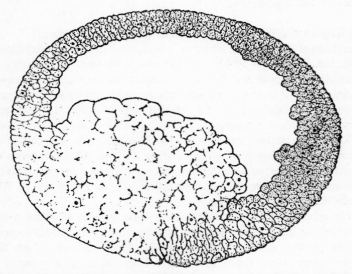

FIG. 5.1 Graded distribution of RNA concentrations in the amphibian gastrula, evidenced by intensity of toluidine blue staining in histological section. (From Brachet, 1950, *Chemical Embryology*, by kind permission of the author.)

In the meantime, Pfautsch (1960) has made a biochemical study of RNA concentrations in isolated parts of the gastrulae of *Triturus alpestris* and *Ambystoma mexicanum*. She obtained somewhat different results from those of Brachet *et al.* in that the highest RNA concentration appeared to be in the dorsal ectoderm rather than in the dorsal lip. Her data are given in Fig. 5.2. It seems most desirable for these results, too, to be repeated before any firm conclusion can be drawn as to the quantitative distribution of RNA in the gastrula.

Since it is now supposed that the sequence of bases on the nucleic acid molecule acts as a code to specify the sequence of amino-acids in the protein (see Crick et al., 1961), the nucleotide composition of nucleic acids in different cell types is a matter of special interest. Some preliminary data (Deuchar and Bristow, 1965) indicate that there are

Concentrations of RNA in Dorsal Ectoderm and Mesoderm of Gastrulae of the Newt, *Triturus alpestris* (Summarized from Pfautsch, 1960)

(Data are given as μg/mg dry weight and are means, $\pm$ standard errors, of five estimations.)

EARLY GASTRULA

Dorsal lip mesoderm	Dorsal ectoderm (not yet induced)
$3 \cdot 25 \pm 0 \cdot 04$	$2 \cdot 68 \pm 0 \cdot 10$

LATE GASTRULA

Archenteron roof mesoderm	Dorsal ectoderm (after induction)
$1 \cdot 78 \pm 0 \cdot 07$	$4 \cdot 46 \pm 0 \cdot 27$

FIG. 5.2

characteristic differences between neural ectoderm, epidermal ectoderm, and endoderm at the early gastrula stage, and that these become more marked as development proceeds. In particular, there is an increase in

Molar Ratios of Nucleotides in Ectoderm of Xenopus Embryos
(From Deuchar and Bristow, 1965)

(Figures are Moles/100 Moles total nucleotides: means, $\pm$ standard errors, from five samples.)

AMP = adenylic acid; GMP = guanidine; CMP = cytidine; UMP = uridine

	AMP	GMP	CMP	UMP
Neural ectoderm				
Early gastrula *	$18 \pm 1 \cdot 8$	$25 \pm 1 \cdot 5$	$31 \pm 0 \cdot 9$	$26 \pm 1 \cdot 2$
Late gastrula *	$24 \pm 1 \cdot 1$	$27 \pm 2 \cdot 2$	$28 \pm 0 \cdot 9$	$21 \pm 1 \cdot 1$
Early neurula	$14 \pm 0 \cdot 6$	$25 \pm 0 \cdot 9$	$40 \pm 1 \cdot 3$	$21 \pm 2 \cdot 5$
Tailbud stage	$23 \pm 1 \cdot 5$	$30 \pm 1 \cdot 3$	$25 \pm 2 \cdot 0$	$22 \pm 0 \cdot 7$
Epidermis				
Early gastrula	$19 \pm 1 \cdot 1$	$17 \pm 1 \cdot 2$	$31 \pm 0 \cdot 3$	$33 \pm 1 \cdot 3$
Late gastrula	$19 \pm 0 \cdot 5$	$27 \pm 1 \cdot 6$	$33 \pm 1 \cdot 8$	$21 \pm 0 \cdot 7$
Early neurula	$19 \pm 0 \cdot 9$	$31 \pm 2 \cdot 5$	$29 \pm 1 \cdot 2$	$21 \pm 0 \cdot 9$
Tailbud stage	$21 \pm 1 \cdot 2$	$25 \pm 1 \cdot 2$	$31 \pm 2 \cdot 3$	$23 \pm 0 \cdot 8$
Neural crest				
Early neurula	$20 \pm 1 \cdot 9$	$27 \pm 1 \cdot 2$	$30 \pm 1 \cdot 7$	$23 \pm 0 \cdot 9$
Tailbud stage	$15 \pm 0 \cdot 5$	$26 \pm 0 \cdot 2$	$29 \pm 0 \cdot 8$	$30 \pm 1 \cdot 6$

* Includes future neural crest.

FIG. 5.3

F

relative concentration of cytidine in the neural plate (Fig. 5.3). The significance of these results cannot be clear until we know more about the base sequences and the stability of the various forms of RNA in these embryonic tissues. It may, however, be postulated that the nucleotide differences are connected with the fact that some specific proteins are being synthesized in each tissue.

(c) Regional differences in the proteins of the gastrula tissues

Different 'types' of protein may be distinguished in small quantities by their immunological properties, electrophoretic mobilities, and enzyme activities. Most studies have been made on whole embryos so far, and

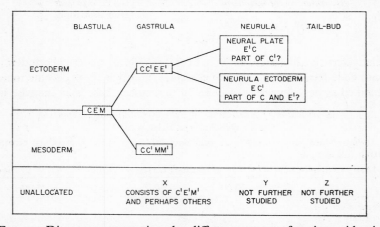

FIG. 5.4 Diagram representing the different groups of antigens identifiable in early embryos of the newt, *Triturus alpestris*. (From Clayton, 1953, by kind permission of the author.)

very little work has been done on separate tissues, mainly owing to the difficulty of collecting enough material for such analyses. In any method that involves laborious dissection of large numbers of embryos, there is a risk that proteins and other cell components may deteriorate during the long time taken to collect the material. A further difficulty with fast-developing forms such as *Xenopus* is that during long time periods the embryos may develop too far before sufficient of a certain stage have been dissected. Despite these difficulties, Clayton (1953) succeeded in demonstrating antigenic differences between ectoderm, mesoderm, and endoderm of newt gastrulae (*Triturus alpestris*). She found that there were characteristic differences including, at the end of gastrulation, differences between neural and epidermal ectoderm (Fig. 5.4). There were also many antigens common to all tissues – as is to be expected in view of the ready interconvertibility of gastrula tissues, shown by grafting experiments.

Relatively little work has been done on the regional distribution of enzymes in the early gastrula. Weber and Boell (1962) measured cytochrome oxidase activity in whole gastrulae of *Xenopus laevis*, but although they later compared dorsal and ventral halves of tailbud stage embryos with respect to a number of enzyme activities they did not achieve any regional comparisons at the gastrula stage. In our own work we have obtained some evidence about protease distribution, which may be mentioned here since it is relevant to one of the major processes of early amphibian development – namely, yolk breakdown. The class of proteases concerned is the cathepsins, which are activated by –SS– and have an optimal pH between 4·0 and 5·0. According to D'Amelio and Ceas (1957) these predominate in dorsal regions of the gastrula of *Discoglossus* (a Corsican frog). I obtained similar results on *Xenopus laevis* (Deuchar, 1958 *b*), but found that when the data were expressed on a *per cell* basis (instead of per unit dry weight or total nitrogen) the cathepsin activity was highest in *ventral* cells. The exact intracellular localization of the cathepsin activity is uncertain. It might be expected to be bound within lysosomes, as in adult tissue, but so far no such particles have been identified with any certainty in amphibian embryos. Billett (1957) has, however, demonstrated β-glucuronidase activity – another enzyme activity characteristic of lysosomes – in developing embryos of *Xenopus laevis*. At least part of the cathepsin activity in *Xenopus* remains bound to the yolk platelets after these have been isolated by centrifuging and then washed several times with saline. It is not clear whether the enzyme is within the platelets, or only adsorbed to their surfaces. This finding, however, supports the view that the chief function of the cathepsin is in the breakdown of yolk protein reserves. The ventral cells have, of course, a higher total yolk content than the dorsal cells and might therefore be expected to be carrying out yolk breakdown on a larger scale than in dorsal cells. The course of yolk utilization during development is now being followed in more detail by a number of electron microscopists, and this topic will be mentioned again in later chapters. Here, we need only emphasize that yolk break-down has already started, even during cleavage stages (Daniel and Yarwood, 1939) and that it results in the addition of peptides and free amino-acids to the 'pool' of raw materials ready for synthesis of new proteins. Dipeptidases, responsible for the last stages of breakdown to form free amino-acids, are also present at the gastrula stage (Pickford, 1943).

(d) Regional differences in the concentrations of free amino-acids

Particular interest accrues from studies of the free amino-acid pattern in different regions of the gastrula, because Roberts and his collaborators (Roberts and Frankel, 1949; Roberts, Lowe, Chanin, and Jelineck, 1957) showed that in different adult tissues these patterns are different and characteristic. A point to be looked for, then, is whether such differences are already beginning to appear in the tissue primordia. Analyses of dorsal lip, of ectoderm and of ventral tissues of the early gastrula, as well as of dorsal and ventral halves of blastulae and of *late* gastrulae, have shown that there are higher concentrations of total free amino-acid in dorsal than in ventral parts. The concentrations of a number of individual amino-acids also showed regional differences (Fig. 5.5). For instance, at the gastrula stage glutamic and aspartic acids were most highly concentrated dorsally, while leucine and valine were present in highest concentrations ventrally. These findings fit with the distribution at later stages, when the central nervous tissue has the highest glutamic acid, aspartic acid, and glutamine concentrations while the heart and blood (derived from ventral regions of the gastrula) have high valine and leucine concentrations. It has been stressed by Ansell and Richter (1954) and confirmed by a number of other authors, that brain tissue of many species contains high concentrations of free glutamine and glutamic acid, which are thought to provide a system for the removal of ammonia that might otherwise accumulate in toxic concentrations owing to blockage of its escape by the 'blood-brain barrier'. (For further discussion of this role of glutamine in the brain, see Meister, 1956; Weil-Malherbe, 1953.) It is most interesting to find

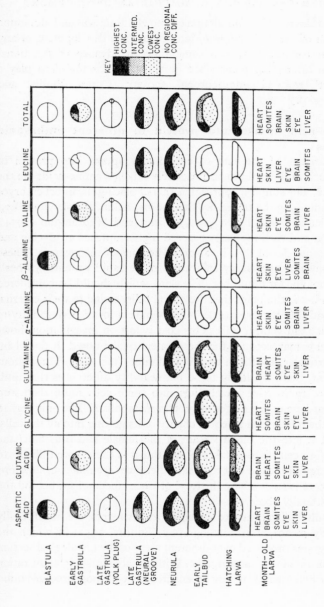

FIG. 5.5 Diagrammatic representation of differences in free amino-acid concentration in embryos of *Xenopus laevis*. (Deuchar, 1956.) Tissues of month-old larva are listed in order of decreasing concentration of amino-acid. Other conventions as in key.

that there is already an accumulation of free glutamic acid and glutamine in the brain of the early embryo, long before the development of any blood-brain barrier. It is also some time in advance of functional activity: an interesting point since glutamic acid is found to play a 'transmitter' role in interneuronal activity (Curtis, Phillis, and Watkins, 1960).

(e) Amino-acid uptake into protein in different embryonic regions

For comparisons of the rate of amino-acid uptake into protein in different parts of the embryo, radioactively-labelled amino-acids are the obvious tool. The simplest approach is that of placing the intact embryos in saline containing the tracer. By this means, Eakin, Kutsky, and Berg (1951), Friedberg and Eakin (1949), Sirlin and Waddington (1954), Waddington and Sirlin (1954) observed higher uptakes of glycine and methionine into dorsal than into ventral regions of the gastrula. These findings may not necessarily indicate a more rapid protein synthesis dorsally, though, for a number of reasons which should be considered critically. First is the point that the dorsal cells, owing to their external 'surface coat' (Holtfreter, 1943) probably have a lower permeability to amino-acids than ventral cells. This coat is lost on invagination, however, and this may account for the greater uptake noted in dorsal lip cells in particular, by Sirlin and Waddington (loc. cit.). Throughout development, there are likely to be permeability differences that limit the entry of radioactive metabolites into some cells more than into others, regardless of their rates of protein metabolism. The only way to introduce the tracer with an equal chance of its getting into all the cells, is to inject it into the blood stream of the female and thus label the oocytes before cell division takes place. But it is then more difficult to assess the significance of any regional differences seen later in development, as there is such a long 'history' of tracer metabolism behind the end-results finally observed.

The results of radioactive labelling experiments are most easily observed by means of autoradiography (Bourne, 1952) in which the density of grains produced over different areas of the histological section gives a measure of the tracer uptake. With suitable washing and fixation procedures beforehand, it can be ensured that all non-protein-bound

Grain Densities in Autoradiographs

Means ± standard errors, of counts on 20 sections in 4 specimens of each stage

GRAINS PER SQUARE (= 144 μ^2 AREA)

STAGE		
Oocytes	*Nucleus*	*Cytoplasm*
	81·3 ± 3·3	37·4 ± 2·2
Unfertilized (2° oocytes)	*Perinuclear region*	*Vegetal cytoplasm*
	58·8 ± 2·0	32·3 ± 4·7
Morulae	*Nucleus*	*Cytoplasm*
	46·9 ± 8·7	18·1 ± 3·8

Blastulae	*Ectoderm*		*Endoderm*	
	Nucleus	*Cytoplasm*	*Nucleus*	*Cytoplasm*
Early blastula	46·7 ± 2·2	27·5 ± 2·7	41·0 ± 2·1	17·8 ± 2·2
Late blastula	46·8 ± 3·4	31·0 ± 3·5	33·9 ± 0·8	27·1 ± 1·4

Gastrulae	*Ectoderm*	*Dorsal mesoderm*	*Endoderm*
Early gastrulae	52·3 ± 4·8	49·9 ± 2·4	36·5 ± 2·5
Mid-gastrulae	31·5 ± 1·1	30·4 ± 3·2	20·1 ± 1·4
Late gastrulae	60·3 ± 2·1	60·0 ± 1·8	33·3 ± 2·3

Later stages	*Neural tissue*	*Chorda*	*Somites*	*Lateral mesoderm*	*Endoderm*	*Ventral ectoderm*
Early neurulae	54·1 ± 1·5	34·85 ± 3·66	51·40 ± 3·17	31·15 ± 2·4	24·2 ± 2·3	36·3 ± 8·8
Late neurulae	55·1 ± 3·6	28·8 ± 7·2	55·9 ± 2·9	33·0 ± 3·0	23·8 ± 3·9	54·0 ± 6·2
Tailbud stage	51·3 ± 4·7	31·5 ± 0·9	52·5 ± 4·5	30·7 ± 2·3	28·9 ± 2·6	54·5 ± 2·4

FIG. 5.6 Distribution of tritium-labelled leucine in insoluble components of tissues of *Xenopus laevis* embryos, after its introduction into proteins of developing oocytes by injection of the female toad. (Deuchar, 1963 *b*.)

Grain Counts in Autoradiographs

Each figure gives the mean counts per graticule square (= 144 μ^2), plus standard error, for counts on 10 different 5 μ sections. At least 5 embryos of each stage were used for counts.

TISSUE OR REGION

STAGE	Nucleus	Cytoplasm
Ovarian oocyte	24·3 ± 5·99	40·7 ± 3·50
Cleavage stages (2–8 cells)	32·2 ± 4·49	46·3 ± 2·67

STAGE	Endoderm	Dorsal mesoderm	Endoderm
Blastula	52·7 ± 2·93	—	53·8 ± 3·49
Early gastrula	33·7 ± 3·30	71·1 ± 3·51	27·0 ± 2·39
Late gastrula	35·6 ± 3·30	44·5 ± 2·85	28·6 ± 7·29

STAGE	Neural tissue	Chorda	Dorsal mesoderm	Lateral mesoderm	Endoderm	Ventral epidermis
Early neurula	64·9 ± 2·27	85·9 ± 4·29	58·3 ± 2·25	50·0 ± 2·95	45·3 ± 3·21	56·2 ± 2·68
Late neurula	56·8 ± 3·93	70·5 ± 5·99	45·2 ± 1·50	49·0 ± 4·00	34·9 ± 2·64	52·9 ± 2·96

STAGE	Neural tube	Chorda[1]	Sclerotome	Dermatome	Myotome	Lateral mesoderm	Endoderm	Ventral epidermis
Tailbud stage	49·8 ± 2·85	69·9 ± 3·85	57·2 ± 2·09	56·6 ± 2·35	32·4 ± 2·47	32·7 ± 1·57	22·4 ± 3·26	49·5 ± 3·45
Hatched larva	74·0 ± 4·84	80·8 ± 6·55	79·6 ± 5·09	73·8 ± 3·65	53·9 ± 3·46	50·0 ± 4·14	35·7 ± 4·40	60·6 ± 2·97
3-day larva	60·0 ± 5·21	89·3 ± 4·97	74·5 ± 3·81	65·5 ± 4·97	38·2 ± 5·58	37·8 ± 1·54	36·3 ± 2·20	63·3 ± 5·78

[1] Chorda sheath, in the 3-day larva.

FIG. 5.7 Distribution of tritium-labelled proline in embryonic tissues of *Xenopus laevis*, in similar experiments to those of Fig. 5.6. (Deuchar, 1964.)

tracer has been removed and that the graining observed is due entirely to uptake into protein. Even so, it is desirable to carry out parallel protein extractions by biochemical methods. The results of this kind of work are shown in Figs. 5.6 and 5.7, which refer to experiments on leucine and proline uptake in *Xenopus laevis* embryos after injection of tritiated amino-acids into the female to label the oocytes (Deuchar, 1963 *b*, 1964). The distributions of the two amino-acids show interesting differences at the gastrula stage. Leucine is present in highest concentration in dorsal parts, whereas proline has a more specific predominance in mesoderm as distinct from other dorsal tissues. As will be seen later (Chapter Eight) the proline (or its derivative, hydroxyproline) then becomes localized more particularly in cartilage and connective tissue-forming parts of the mesoderm which are synthesizing collagen. Collagen is the only protein so far known to contain substantial quantities of hydroxyproline.

Ceas and Naselli (1958) have used similar methods to study the distribution of S35-methionine in *Discoglossus* embryos after injection into the female frog. They found that more of the amino-acid became bound to protein in ventral regions than in dorsal regions of the gastrula. In dorsal regions there was more methionine in the TCA-soluble fraction, suggesting that it had been freed during the breakdown of yolk protein. Methionine is not, like hydroxyproline, specific to any one type of protein, so it can only be used as an indicator of general events of protein metabolism. The whole embryo, and particularly its yolk, has a high proportion of sulphur-containing proteins, and would therefore be expected to be rich in methionine.

Ranzi drew attention some time ago to the fact that in dorsal regions of both echinoderm and amphibian embryos, the proteins are, on the whole, less viscous and more soluble than those in ventral regions. He suggested that the actions of lithium chloride and of sodium sulphocyanide – agents which, respectively, reduce and enlarge the notochord and have consequent effects on the central nervous system, too – could be explained in terms of their effects on protein solubility. Lithium ions increase the viscosity of proteins and decrease their solubility: sulphocyanide has the opposite effect. This work, which has been reviewed by Ranzi (1962), emphasizes the fact that, in dorsal regions of the early embryo, proteins are mobilized more rapidly than in ventral regions.

(f) Regional distribution of other metabolites in the early gastrula

Tracer techniques can, of course, also be applied to measurements of the uptake of many other precursors into the constituents of embryonic tissue. Nucleotides, for instance, can be used to assess the sites and rates of nucleic acid synthesis in the early embryo. Ficq (1960) and Sirlin (1958) pioneered in the methods, and Rounds and Flickinger (1958) have used tracers particularly in studies of the passage of material from the invaginating mesoderm into the neural plate during neural induction: a topic that will be discussed further in Chapter Seven. The interest of most authors has, in fact, centred either on oocyte stages or on stages from gastrulation onwards. One observation on events during gastrulation may be mentioned: Warner and Finamore (1962) found that the labelling and the concentration of (free) adenosine triphosphate and guanidine triphosphate decreased during gastrulation. This is interesting in view of our own findings (Deuchar and Bristow, above) that the molar proportions of the corresponding mononucleotides in RNA decreases (while cytidine increases proportionately), during gastrulation.

(g) The origins of the regional differences

It has already been pointed out in an earlier chapter that there are differential distributions of the cytoplasmic components of the future embryo from oocyte stages onwards. The most marked differential 'gradient' runs from animal to vegetal pole, with increasing density and size of yolk platelets as its main feature. Other components such as mitochondria, RNA, and cytoplasmic DNA are also unequally distributed (see Chapter 3). It is self-evident that the regional differences appearing in the embryo derive partly from this original state of affairs in the oocyte. But it is equally clear, from the known adaptability of the embryonic cells at early stages, that whatever determinants are carried in their cytoplasm must be readily modifiable. Since the particulate components of the cytoplasm cannot cross cell boundaries, they must be capable of numerical adjustment within each cell, in response to changing environmental conditions. One of the first effects of any external change, then, would be to alter the cytoplasmic constitution of the cells. Electron microscope studies (Eakin and Lehmann, 1957;

Karasaki, 1959 *a* and *b*; Butschak, 1960) have already demonstrated divergent trends of ultrastructure in the cells of the early embryo, but the results are too preliminary for any general conclusions to be drawn from them yet. So far, it appears that cells of the different regions of the gastrula differ only in the quantity and not in the kind of cytoplasmic structures they contain.

In conclusion, it must again be stressed that one of the ways in which embryonic cells exhibit their differentiation is by their motile behaviour. They show greater adhesive affinity to cells of their own kind than to cells from other regions, and also have inherent tendencies to carry out the movements characteristic of gastrulation and neurulation. Thus dorsal lip cells tend to invaginate, while epidermal cells tend to spread out over the surface of other gastrula cells. The source of these differences, and the biochemical events that accompany them, will be dealt with further in the succeeding chapter.

CHAPTER SIX

Biochemical Events During Gastrulation

It is little wonder that the peculiar phenomenon of gastrulation has attracted so much interest. What, we must still question, causes the cells of the embryo at this stage in their life-history suddenly to start to undergo organized mass movements, differing characteristically according to what tissues they are going to form? This problem has been approached from the same two angles described in preceding chapters: *in toto* observations and observations on isolated parts of the embryo.

Seen in retrospect, it is remarkable how much of this research, like that in many other biological fields recently, has been influenced by current 'fashions' of thought, as well as by the availability of certain techniques. It is very rare to find an exclusively logical series of investigations: ideas that happen to be popular, or expediencies of each research worker's own particular environment, often lead to a change of procedure or policy and result in unanticipated discoveries outside the original intent of the investigation. Nearly always, this is a good thing. But sometimes 'fashions' of thought are harmful: if they last too long, they result in stagnation of ideas.

(a) Factors initiating gastrulation

In attempted explanations of the causes of gastrulation in amphibians, at least four 'fashions' of thought have played prominent parts: surface tension, osmotic pressure, pH and (still with its supporters) oxygen tension. We shall consider these in turn.

Those who used to think that surface tension changes could account for the inward movement of dorsal lip cells at the beginning of gastrulation had in mind a 'liquid drop' model of the cell. Subsequent work on the nature of the cell surface has shown how misleading this liquid drop analogy was (cf. also Spek's theory of cleavage, p. 54). Although gastrula cells certainly react to surface-active agents such as detergents attempts to modify their movements by these agents have not given consistent or informative results. Such experiments are in any case complicated by the special properties of the outer cells' 'surface coat' to

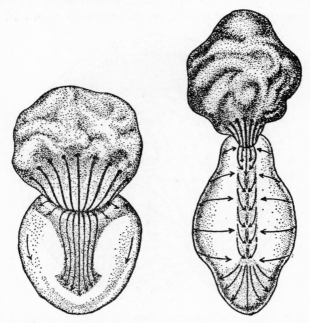

FIG. 6.1 Holtfreter's 'exogastrula', produced by exposure to hypertonic saline. Arrows show tissue movements. (From Spemann, *Embryonic Development and Induction*, 1938.)

which Holtfreter (1943) first drew attention. This surface coat is lost in detergents. It is also lost by the gastrula cells during their normal invagination in the intact embryo. However, no amount of treatment of embryos with detergents will influence the timing or course of the invagination process. Hence this line of investigation has fallen out of popularity, although we still have much to learn about the surface tension properties of gastrula cells and how these may influence their behaviour, as well as about the nature of the surface coat (Løvtrup, 1962).

Holtfreter was, in the 1930s, leader of another fashion in investigation: that of the effects of changes in osmotic pressure on gastrulation movements. In one of his most famous experiments (1933 *b*) he produced an 'exogastrula' (Fig. 6.1), in which the mesoderm *evaginated* instead of invaginating, by leaving the embryo in hypertonic saline. If, as his

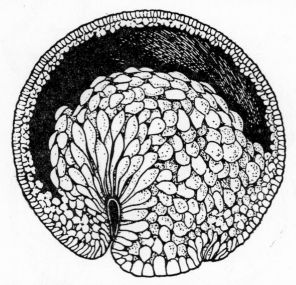

FIG. 6.2 Drawing of early gastrula, showing change in shape of cells as they invaginate (somewhat diagrammatic). (Reproduced from Waddington, 1956, *Principles of Embryology*.)

experiment implied, the mesoderm cells move towards a hypertonic medium, one should expect the blastocoel fluid to be hypertonic to the external surroundings (capsular fluid) of the embryo and thus to account for the normal *inward* movement of the mesoderm cells. Unfortunately, Holtfreter's first experiment has never been followed up by any systematic study of the effects of a range of saline tonicities on the movement of the mesoderm cells. His detailed drawings of the shape of the dorsal lip cells as they invaginate, which are often reproduced in textbooks (cf. Fig. 6.2) are, however, suggestive of a differential water uptake in these cells. If water passed from the exterior into the blastocoel by simple osmosis, through these cells, this might explain their change in shape to a bottle-shape with the widest end innermost (Fig. 6.3). This change could in itself result in the formation of the blastopore groove. However, no one has ever directly demonstrated the passage of water through these cells (by deuterium-labelling, for instance). Moreover, since it is known that cell membranes do not behave like simple

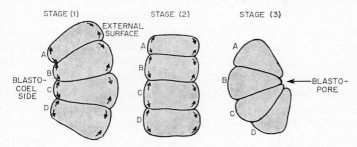

FIG. 6.3 Simplified diagram illustrating how a reversal of shape of cells could result in the formation of a blastopore groove.

semi-permeable membranes, but are capable of absorption against osmotic gradients, a simple 'osmotic' theory is unlikely to account for any form of cell- or tissue-movement in embryos.

It is interesting that Kocher-Becker et al. (1965) have obtained a form of exogastrulation, in which the *endoderm* eventually comes to lie *outside the ectoderm*, after implanting a purified mesoderm-inducing protein into the blastocoel in the newt, *Triturus*. They explain the effect as chiefly due to a change in the behaviour of the ectoderm cells, which no longer carry out epibolic movements because they are converted into mesoderm. This is a more durable interpretation than the old-fashioned one based entirely on differential absorption of water, even though it still leaves unsolved the problem of *how* the inductor protein has changed the behaviour of the cells. More will be said later (p. 88f.) about the biochemical mechanisms of these different gastrulation movements of epiboly and invagination.

The idea that pH differences between external and internal media might be responsible for the invagination of mesoderm in the gastrula has also been entertained. But measurements of pH on such small volumes of fluid as that in the blastocoel are extremely difficult and no clear or reliable data have emerged. Treatment of gastrulae with either alkali or acid has produced no effects except varying degrees of damage to the cells, although at later stages, it appears, ectoderm of certain species may undergo neurulation in the presence of alkali (Barth, 1941; Holtfreter, 1947).

It remains to consider whether oxygen tension may affect the invagination of mesoderm and thus influence the onset of gastrulation. There have been numerous reports that the dorsal lip has a higher respiration rate and oxygen consumption than other regions of the gastrula (see Chapter Five). Løvtrup and Pigon (1958), interestingly, claimed that oxygen tension influences the position of the dorsal lip. When blastulae were placed in capillary tubes so as to be exposed to oxygen at one side only, the dorsal lip always appeared at this side. The possibility that the embryos rotated before they started to gastrulate was not excluded, however. Nor is it clear how in normal development the dorsal lip could acquire a better oxygen supply than other regions, unless its cells have a higher permeability to oxygen. It is possible that the grey crescent cortex confers some such enhanced permeability on dorsal lip cells, but this remains to be proved (cf. Løvtrup, 1965).

(b) Metabolism during gastrulation
The process of gastrulation is one of intense activity. It is not surprising, then, that it should be an important turning-point of embryonic metabolism. It is remarkable how many of the published time graphs of concentrations of metabolites or of activities of enzymes during development show a point of upward inflection at the time of onset of gastrulation (e.g. Løvtrup, 1955; cf. also Chapter Ten). This upward inflexion is shown particularly clearly in curves of cytochrome oxidase activity and of oxygen consumption – both indicators of respiration rate. Hence it is not surprising that treatments that deprive an embryo of its oxygen supply or block its cytochrome oxidase activity cause an arrest of gastrulation. In the arrested gastrulae (which can be obtained by many other treatments, too) most of the parameters that should increase during gastrulation do not do so, but remain constant until the embryo is either

restored to normal or eventually dies under continued treatment. Both DNA and RNA synthesis are inhibited when gastrulation is blocked: this was first shown by Brachet (see 1960) after subjecting embryos to heat 'shock' treatments at 37° C. The same cessation of synthesis occurs in hybrids which fail to go beyond the gastrula stage (Chen, 1953). Although the usual end of these arrested embryos is death, Rosenbaum (1960) was able to delay the onset of autolysis and consequently to keep the gastrulae alive for periods of several days, by increased oxygen tensions. His work does not, however, lend any support to Løvtrup and Pigon's view (loc. cit.) that oxygen tension has some determining influence on gastrulation, since none of the embryos he treated ever continued to gastrulate.

Cells of the gastrula which for one reason or another do not establish normal topographical relationships with other tissues may, at the end of a phase of abnormal movements, undergo complete disaggregation. This often happens when small pieces of tissue are grown in non-ideal culture conditions. Disaggregation may also be produced by treatment with agents like 'Versene' that bind calcium ions (Curtis, 1957). The remarkable feature of such experimentally-produced disaggregates is that, if the cells are healthy, they readily reaggregate as soon as they are returned to normal saline, and even reform a complete embryo by a process of differential reassortment and re-adhesion. Townes and Holtfreter (1955) have described this behaviour of the cells in some detail. They have also cultured gastrula and neurula cells in different combinations, finding that they behave characteristically with respect to the other cell-types: mesoderm will always invaginate into ectoderm and neural plate into epidermis. No satisfactory explanation in biochemical terms has yet been found for this selective behaviour of the different cell-types. Some time ago Weiss (1947) suggested that there were stereochemically specific end-groups at the cell surface, which 'fitted' to the surface end-groups of like cells and so enabled them to stick to their own kind, but not to other kinds of cells. This is somewhat analogous to the supposed 'fit' of antigen end-groups to an antibody. Spiegel (1954) did, in fact, find evidence that some antigen–antibody type of mechanism was involved in these cell adhesions, for he prevented the reaggregation of gastrula cells of *Rana pipiens* by treating them with antiserum to that species, whereas antiserum to *Triturus alpestris* had no such effect.

G

In an interesting recent discussion Steinberg (1965) has argued, however, that the cell-affinities could result simply from quantitative differences in their surface patterns and that no specific molecular 'fit' need be postulated. Further investigation of the possibility that cell-specific antigens control the selective adhesions and movements of gastrula cells is most desirable.

Investigation of the behaviour of isolated gastrula cells is, of course, the *second* angle of approach mentioned at the beginning of this chapter. There are still hardly any conclusive biochemical findings to report in this field. Gregg and Ornstein (1952) attempted to find out what particular types of metabolism characterize the markedly different movements of epiboly, invagination, and fusion that are distinctive properties of ectoderm and mesoderm respectively. Their results of treating gastrula cells with inhibitors are given in Fig. 6.4. Although

	CELLULAR PROCESSES EXAMINED IN EXPLANTS			
	1	2	3	4
Inhibitors made up in Holtfreter's solution, pH 8·0	*Endoderm fuses into endoderm by formation of bottle-shaped cells*	*Notochord stretching on endoderm as during invagination*	*Ectoderm spreading over endoderm as during epiboly*	*Fusion of meso-derm with ecto-derm on top of endoderm*
2–4-Dinitrophenol	Normal	Normal	Inhibited	Normal
95 N_2 : 5 CO_2	Normal	Normal	Inhibited	Normal
Azide	Normal	Suppressed	Suppressed	Normal
p-Chloromercuri-benzoic acid	Normal	Suppressed	Suppressed	Indeterminate
Urethane	Normal	Suppressed	Normal	Normal
Sodium barbital	Suppressed	Suppressed	Suppressed	Normal
Sodium malonate 0·045M	Suppressed	Suppressed	Suppressed	Suppressed
Sodium chloride, 0·045M	Normal	Normal	Suppressed	Normal

FIG. 6.4 Effects of chemical inhibitors on morphogenetic movements of gastrula cells. (Gregg and Ornstein, 1952: reproduced from Barth and Barth, 1954, *The Energetics of Development*.)

each type of movement appears to be inhibited by more than one agent, some general points emerge. One is that the spreading of ectoderm is by far the most easily inhibited. This movement (epiboly) appears to require adequate functioning of phosphate exchange (inhibited by di-nitrophenol), of respiration and –SH groups (blocked by benzoic acid), and also to require normal osmotic conditions and sodium ion con-centration (altered by the 0·045M sodium chloride). The stretching of notochord cells was the only movement of those tested that was in-hibited by urethane, one of the respiratory depressants. It was also more

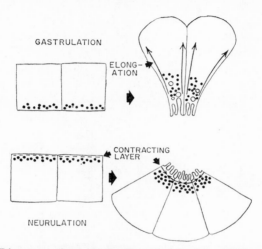

GASTRULATION

ELONG-
ATION

CONTRACTING
LAYER

NEURULATION

FIG. 6.5 Diagrams of the mechanisms involved in cell shape changes at gastrulation and neurulation. (From Balinsky, 1960 b.)

susceptible to azide (which blocks cytochrome oxidase activity) than were the other, 'settling down and fusion' movements of mesoderm and endoderm, that occur normally at the end of gastrulation. As a whole, Gregg and Ornstein's results indicate that both the stretching involved in ectoderm epiboly and the stretching of mesoderm after its invagina-tion depend heavily on a high rate of respiration, and that the epiboly depends, in addition, on phosphate transfer being properly linked to oxidations. This latter dependence suggests similarities to muscle con-traction and may indicate that an ATPase mechanism is involved in the movement.

The importance of ATPase, similar to the enzyme of myosin, for many types of cellular movements and changes of shape has been emphasized by the work of Hoffman-Berling (1954) and his followers. He has demonstrated that the contractility of many different cells, and of cell-organelles such as flagella, is stimulated by ATP. Among

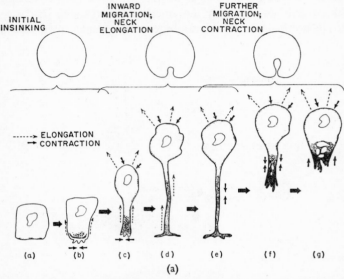

FIG. 6.6 (*a*) Scheme of cell shape changes at blastopore groove, as seen by electron microscopy. (*b*) Detail of the blastopore groove cells. (From Baker, 1965, with kind permission of the author.) Theoretical scheme for the transformations of a blastoporal cell during gastrulation, based on the hypothesis of contraction and expansion of the dense layer. The end of the cell neck remains securely adherent to adjacent cells. (*a*) The cell as it appears on the surface prior to gastrulation. (*b*) The distal surface contracts causing initial insinking of the blastoporal pit. (*c*), (*d*) The proximal cell surface begins to migrate inward, deepening the groove; the distal surface continues to contract and the neck elongates. (*e*), (*f*), (*g*) The neck contracts after it reaches maximum elongation. This shortening, together with the pull exerted by the migrating inner ends, furthers invagination and pulls adjacent cells into the groove. Some flask cells bypass stages (*d*) and (*e*). ac = archenteron cavity; bg = blastopore groove; fc = flask cell; wc = wedge cell; i = intercellular space; p = pseudopodium-like process; sm = specialized mesoderm cell; l = lipid droplet; m = mitochondrion; ml = membranous layer; vc = vacuole; y = yolk platelet.

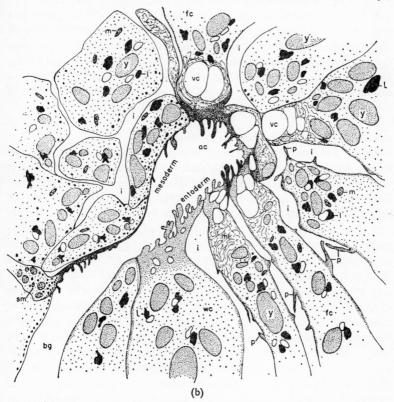

(b)

embryonic cells, only chick myoblasts have so far been shown to respond to ATP by contracting visibly (Holtzer, Marshall, and Finck, 1957). Somite-forming cells of late gastrulae of *Xenopus* will reaggregate more rapidly in the presence of ATP (Deuchar, 1961 *a*). It would be interesting to know if other gastrula cells are as sensitive to ATP as are those of the future somite, or whether this is a property peculiar to myoblasts. The somite cells have also been shown to have ATPase activity, which may presage the formation of myosin in some of them. But a great deal of further investigation is necessary in order to decide whether an ATPase mechanism of cell-movement is a general phenomenon in amphibian gastrulation or is restricted only to certain types of cell.

Focusing attention again on the intact embryo, Baker (1965) has suggested, from an electron microscope study of blastopore lip cells in the gastrula of the tree-frog, *Hyla regilla*, that the dense, subsurface cytoplasm at their distal ends contains microfibrils and is contractile. Balinsky (1960 *b*) advanced a similar suggestion of contractile bands to explain gastrulation and neurulation. His and Baker's interpretations of the ultrastructural changes are given in Figs. 6.5 and 6.6.

(c) The events of 'chemodifferentiation'

Some of the biochemical events that occur in the intact embryo during gastrulation have already been dealt with in detail in the last chapter, so we shall only repeat the chief of these here. Among the most important features are respiration and RNA concentration. For both of these, the same could be said: namely, that in the early gastrula there is a gradient with its highest point at the dorsal lip, and that this dorso-ventral gradient persists, but with neural ectoderm instead of mesoderm at its highest point, in the late gastrula. Clearly, either the mesoderm loses some of its respiratory activity and RNA, or the dorsal ectoderm acquires more of these, perhaps as a result of its contact with mesoderm of the archenteron roof. It is unlikely, however, that the change-over of supremacy is a large one, since it will be recalled that there have been dissenters (Barth and Sze, 1951; Pfautsch, 1960) to the general view, who have obtained highest figures for the ectoderm and not the meso-derm. There is certainly a more rewarding future in detailed, rather than overall studies of RNA during gastrulation. It would be of great interest, for instance, to know how soon there are detectable changes in base composition of different forms of RNA in different cell-types of the gastrula. The finding of an increased relative molar concentration of cytidine in the neural plate ectoderm during gastrulation (Deuchar and Bristow, 1965), which has already been mentioned (p. 71) has provided a stimulating suggestion that other short-term changes related to specific interactions between tissues of the gastrula may await discovery.

Clayton's work (1953), referred to in the last chapter, also pointed particularly to changes in the neural plate ectoderm, for by the end of gastrulation this tissue is distinguishable antigenically from epidermis, whereas the two are indistinguishable in their antigen complement at the early gastrula stage. We do not yet know exactly when the antigenic changes occur: it should be possible to follow this by fluorescent antibody staining methods, however. A point that has emerged from work by Romanovsky (1964) (referred to in more detail in Chapter Ten) should be emphasized here. This is, that differentiation of the gastrula cells involves *losses* of specific antigens as well as the acquisition of new ones. Evidently, protein breakdown plays just as essential a role as synthesis, not only in providing raw materials but also in getting rid of obsolescent types of protein. We must envisage special and different modes of protein breakdown in different cells of the gastrula and at

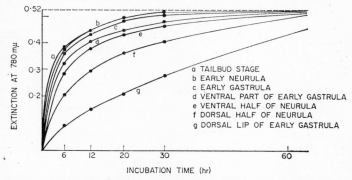

FIG. 6·7 Time curves for cathepsin activity in different regions of *Xenopus laevis* embryos. (Deuchar, 1958.)

different stages of gastrulation, therefore, since there is no possibility of large-scale transfers of protein from one cell-type to another intact.

As has already been indicated, intracellular cathepsins are highly active in early embryonic cells and are probably the main agents in protein breakdown. We know nothing, however, of possible differences in *kinds* of cathepsin present in different tissues. The preliminary findings (Deuchar, 1958 *b*) show that there are characteristically different time curves for cathepsin activity in different regions of the gastrula (Fig. 6.7). This, in itself, could lead to differences in rates of breakdown of different kinds of protein in the regions – a possible basis for explaining the different antigen losses demonstrated by Romanovsky.

Another possibility to be borne in mind when considering distributions of enzyme activity during gastrulation is that the enzyme may be synthesized in different concentrations in different regions. These quantitative differences could gradually lead to a wide divergence in tissue metabolism. It is probable that most enzyme activity differences between different adult tissues are quantitative ones, since very few enzymes are known that are peculiar to one tissue only.

One example of a well-known tissue-specific enzyme is tryptophan peroxidase (or pyrrolase), which in the adult is found only in the liver. It catalyzes the first, oxidative step in tryptophan breakdown (Fig. 6.8). In some laudable pioneer work Stearns and Kostellow (1958) claimed that the activity of this enzyme could be enhanced tenfold in frog

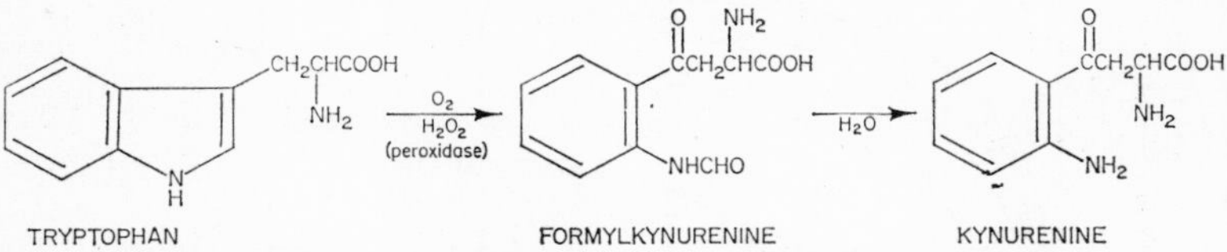

FIG. 6.8 Reaction catalysed by tryptophan peroxidase.

gastrula cells when they were grown in the presence of tryptophan. This seemed a clear case of enzyme induction, similar to that demonstrable in the adult liver treated with tryptophan (Lee, 1956). Stearns and Kostellow found that at the end of gastrulation the enhancement of activity was demonstrable only in endoderm cells, and not in the other types, whereas it was demonstrable in *all* early gastrula cells. So they apparently had a beautiful example of a special kind of biochemical differentiation taking place in endoderm cells during gastrulation. But, unfortunately, other investigators who have tried to repeat their work have not been able to demonstrate induction of tryptophan peroxidase until much later stages of development (Spiegel and Frankel, 1961). More unfortunately still, the lack of success with this enzyme has discouraged others from looking for further examples of enzyme induction in early amphibian embryos. Limited successes have been achieved with chick embryos, however (Gordon and Roder, 1953), and there is no reason to doubt that enzyme induction occurs during embryonic development.

A particular enzyme activity that is essential to protein synthesis of all kinds is amino-acid activation (Hoagland, Keller and Zamecnik, 1956). Fig. 6.9 gives a summary of the reaction. It was pointed out in the last chapter that the uptake of amino-acids appears to differ both in kind and quantity, in different regions of the gastrula. The very preliminary data available so far show that leucine activation is more marked in ventral than in dorsal regions of the early gastrula. This, if it means anything, must indicate that more leucine is being taken up into protein in the ventral regions. One leucine-rich protein that is synthesized ventrally is haemoglobin, but at this early stage it could only be precursors that were forming: haemoglobin itself does not appear until after hatching. Another protein that is particularly rich in leucine is myosin: it is interesting therefore that later, at the tailbud stage, somite tissue shows the highest leucine-activating activity of those regions tested (Deuchar, 1961 b). There is, at the same time, a fall in the concentration of free leucine in these dorsal tissues, suggesting that it is being taken up into protein particularly rapidly.

(1) Amino-acid + ATP $\underset{}{\overset{E_1}{\rightleftharpoons}}$ amino-acid − AMP − E_1 (+ PP)

(2) Amino-acid − AMP − E_1
$\qquad$ + soluble RNA $\underset{}{\overset{E_2}{\rightleftharpoons}}$ amino-acid − RNA (+ AMP + E_1)

(3) Amino-acid − RNA
$\qquad$ + RNP $\underset{\substack{GTP \\ ATP}}{\overset{E_3}{\longrightarrow}}$ peptide chain − RNP (microsomes)

FIG. 6.9 Scheme of the reactions in amino-acid activation. (After Zamecnik et al., 1958.)

In the foregoing examples we may now have the beginnings of some meaning for the term 'chemodifferentiation' which has so often been used in the past to describe our areas of ignorance as to how cells become 'set' on a particular course of development. Their 'set' is acquired during gastrulation, so that they are no longer multipotential as they are at the beginning of gastrulation. Probably the most clear-cut of the biochemical differences between late gastrula tissues that we know about so far are the antigenic ones (Clayton, 1953; Inoue, 1961 a and b; Romanovsky, 1964). All the other features that we have mentioned are quantitative and many are linked, i.e. the differences in cathepsin

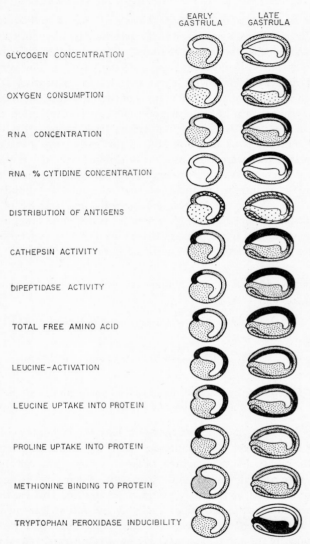

	EARLY GASTRULA	LATE GASTRULA
GLYCOGEN CONCENTRATION		
OXYGEN CONSUMPTION		
RNA CONCENTRATION		
RNA % CYTIDINE CONCENTRATION		
DISTRIBUTION OF ANTIGENS		
CATHEPSIN ACTIVITY		
DIPEPTIDASE ACTIVITY		
TOTAL FREE AMINO ACID		
LEUCINE-ACTIVATION		
LEUCINE UPTAKE INTO PROTEIN		
PROLINE UPTAKE INTO PROTEIN		
METHIONINE BINDING TO PROTEIN		
TRYPTOPHAN PEROXIDASE INDUCIBILITY		

FIG. 6.10 Summary diagram of the main changes in distribution of bio-chemical constituents that occur during gastrulation. Relative concentrations are indicated by relative depth of shading.

activity, free amino-acid content, and amino-acid activating activity. They could, with perhaps some differential enzyme inductions in different regions, cause further qualitative differences to emerge gradually during gastrulation. Fig. 6.10 summarizes the changes in distribution of biochemical properties between the beginning and end of gastrulation. But this figure omits any integrative explanation of the events that go on continuously during gastrulation. There is, in actual fact, a dearth of biochemical data on *mid*-gastrulae, mainly because of the difficulty of defining and collecting enough of these intermediate stages during an experiment. The embryologist usually hopes to be able to prove his point from data on early and late gastrulae only. We shall probably never be able to fill in the intervening gaps satisfactorily, until we have some means of *in vivo* observation of biochemical processes in developing gastrulae and it is no longer necessary to collect and kill large numbers of embryos in order to make measurements on them.

This same failing – the lack of knowledge about mid-gastrulation stages – is met with in the work on neural induction, one of the most important events taking place during the period of gastrulation and neurulation. Because of its importance and the volume of research that has been devoted to it, this topic will be dealt with next, in a separate chapter.

CHAPTER SEVEN

Biochemical Events in the Amphibian Neurula

The morphological characteristics of the neurula stage have already been described in Chapter Two. Their appearance is preceded by the event known as 'neural induction', which may be defined as an influence on the dorsal ectoderm, normally exerted by the dorsal mesoderm of the archenteron roof, causing this ectoderm to start differentiating into a neural plate. Probably more experimental work has been concentrated on this event than on any other phenomenon of early amphibian development. Numerous investigators have been involved and the scope of their investigations has, in fact, been far broader than 'necessary' for the solution of the problem. The obvious, though tedious, experiments that would obtain the required answer directly have so far been omitted, however. Since there are very good reviews of the subject in recent textbooks (e.g. Balinsky, 1960 c; Saxen and Toivönen, 1962), only a few examples of the types of experimental evidence and the conclusions we may reach from them will be mentioned in the critique that follows here.

The crucial questions about neural induction that require answering are these: what are the substances in the inducing mesoderm of the embryo that are responsible for changing the course of differentiation in the ectoderm, and how do they do so? There are, again, two ways of investigating this, comparable with the two methods of approach distinguished in previous chapters. One, which we can call the 'in situ' method, involves labelling the gastrula mesoderm either with radioactive tracers or with fluorescent antibodies and then examining sections of the embryo at a later stage to see whether the particular materials labelled have passed across to the ectoderm. The other, biochemical method, involves fractionation of extracts from an inducer tissue and testing the various fractions as inductors by implanting them (in some compact form such as a coagulum) into an embryo or into a vesicle of ectoderm. Both these approaches have been amply used, but always somewhat inconclusively, hence our information about the nature of neural induction, although voluminous, remains incomplete. We still do not know exactly what inducing agent from the mesoderm acts upon the dorsal ectoderm in the normal embryo. So the problem of *how* it does so and how, in biochemical terms, ectoderm is turned into neural plate is necessarily unsolved too. It must be stressed, too, that we do not know what are the *essential* features distinguishing neural plate biochemically from other kinds of tissue in the gastrula. One or two of its qualitatively distinctive features have been mentioned already: for instance, its high concentrations of free glutamic acid and glutamine, the high relative molar concentration of cytidine in its RNA and the appearance of at least some antigenically distinct proteins. But it still remains a theoretical possibility that other tissues may be capable of acquiring these same features and nevertheless *not* turn into neural plate. It seems unlikely, in fact, that differences of the kinds just mentioned are diagnostic of neural tissue or crucial in determining its differentiation – with the possible exception of its antigenic make-up. But the latter requires much more detailed analysis than was achieved by Clayton (1953) in her pioneering work (cf. Chapter Five, p. 72).

All these remarks amount to an admission that we still do not know the biochemical nature of the changes whose *induction* has so long been studied. Have not the investigators been 'putting the cart before the horse'? It is usual in biochemical work to know the course of a reaction before going on to investigate the conditions that control it. As with all embryological research, however, the biochemical work has been built on to what were originally much less precise criteria for 'reactions' and 'control systems'. Thus, the reaction called 'neural differentiation' still means, to all investigators, simply what is seen morphologically as the appearance of a pale, slipper-shaped plate of ectoderm on the dorsal surface of the embryo or explant, and the rolling up of this plate to form a tube. So, in what follows we shall be dealing with some of the enormous number of investigations on biochemical factors that may govern the appearance of this distinct morphological entity, the neural tube.

For convenience, the 'extraction' approach will be considered first and the '*in situ*' observations and future possibilities dealt with afterwards.

(a) Investigations of neural induction by 'extraction' procedures

Extraction involves, first, killing the cells. This first step was taken by Holtfreter in his classic experiments (1933 *a*) in which he dipped the dorsal lip into boiling water before implanting it into a gastrula. He obtained good neural inductions, which provided the first indication that the induction was a biochemical process and did not depend on integrity of the cells. The group of workers in Cambridge led by Waddington and Needham in the 1930s then went on to test extracts of dorsal lip tissue as inductors – chiefly the sterol fraction which they found to be most effective. The methods which they and their contemporaries were employing in what became a competitive 'gold-rush' to discover 'the organizer substance' would seem crude to present-day biochemists, however. Hard on the heels of this preliminary work with extracts of the dorsal lip tissue came a spate of work in which all kinds of tissues, some of them mammalian in origin, were implanted into the embryo or used as sources of biochemical extracts for implantation. *So many* of these materials proved to be successful inductors that it became clear that the process of neural differentiation could easily be set off by a very wide variety of non-specific stimuli which probably bore no resemblance to the mode of induction in the normal embryo. Figure 7.1 gives examples of the many agents that were found capable of stimulating neural differentiation. Looking at the long list, one cannot help sharing the scepticism which Holtfreter expressed in his suggestion (1947) that all these inductions were due simply to a partial cytolysis, liberating materials from the embryo's own cells that then acted as inductors. Both he and Barth (1941) had been able to show that mere alkali treatment of isolated ectoderm of some salamander species caused it to neuralize after some cytolysis had taken place.

The 'extraction' work on induction entered a second phase after the Second World War, when two main schools, Yamada's in Japan and Toivönen's in Finland, started to use improved biochemical fractionation procedures, such as differential centrifugation, precipitation of ribonucleoprotein by streptomycin sulphate, and separation of protein components by electrophoresis. Attention was concentrated chiefly on

	DISTRIBUTION OF THE PRIMARY EVOCATOR		
	Weak inductions; e.g. neuroid thickenings, palisades, etc.	Strong neural inductions; e.g. small neural tubes or cavities	Very strong neural inductions; e.g. big brains
Mammals			
Homo sapiens	—	—	T, K, L, B, t
Mus musculus	b, F	l, npl	K, L, B, A, H
Bos taurus	—	L	L, Me
Birds			
Gallus domesticus	—	npl	ee, B
Lanius minor		T, K, L, S, A, F	—
Reptiles			
Lacerta agilis	—	K, S	L
Amphibia			
Rana esculenta	—	M, r	L, Me
Triton alpestris	r	H, Lb	B, L, C
Salamandra maculosa	L, H	—	B, r
Fishes			
Gasterosteus aculeatus	—	—	H, o, M, L
Insects			
Libellula sp.?	F	N	—
Deilephila euphorbiae	N	pl	—
Vanessa urticae	id	—	—
Molluscs			
Limnaea stagnalis	fM	L	—
Planorbis corneus	fM	—	—
Crustacea			
Daphnia pulex	—	e	—
Worms			
Ligula simplicissima	sob	—	—
Enchytraeus albidus	M	—	—
Coelenterates			
Hydra viridis	sob	—	—

T, thyroid	o, ovarian eggs	Lb, limb-bud
K, kidney	e, extract	pl, pupal lymph
B, brain	ee, embryo extract	id, imaginal discs
L, liver	l, lens	sob, section of whole body
t, tongue	S, testis	fM, foot muscle
H, heart	F, adipose tissue	Me, muscle extract
A, adrenals	N, nerve tissue	npl, tumour
r, retina	b, blood	
M, muscle	C, cartilage	

FIG. 7.1 Table illustrating the wide variety of tissues found capable of neural induction. (From Needham, 1942, *Biochemistry and Morphogenesis*, by kind permission of the author.)

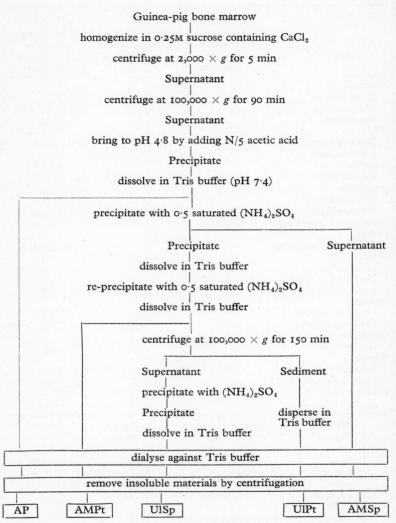

FIG. 7.2 Scheme of Yamada's fractionation procedure to isolate inducing factors from bone marrow. (Yamada, 1960.)

the three mammalian (guinea-pig) tissues that had been found to give most numerous and specific inductions. These were liver, kidney, and bone marrow, which induced, respectively, forebrain, hindbrain and spinal cord, and *mesoderm*, in highest proportions. Yamada's team were able eventually to isolate from *liver* a particular ribonucleoprotein component that induced forebrain in much higher proportion than the original tissue. Later, he isolated from *bone marrow* an acid-soluble protein, responsible for the mesoderm induction. His fractionation procedure and results are given diagrammatically in Fig. 7.2. An even purer mesoderm-inducing factor, which is a protein of molecular weight less than 3,000, has been isolated from chick embryos by Tiedemann and his collaborators using chromatography on carboxymethyl cellulose, and zone electrophoresis (Tiedemann et al., 1961). Both neural and mesodermal inductors are inactivated by proteolytic enzymes but *not* by RNAase (Tiedemann, loc. cit., for reference).

The recent work in Tiedemann's laboratory in Germany has since brought us much nearer to the situation in the normal embryo. Tiedemann's team have isolated distinct components from whole gastrulae and neurulae, that induce different regions of the brain or spinal cord (Fig. 7.3). One of their most interesting, but so far unexplained, findings was that phenol treatment caused mesoderm-inducing ability to appear. More recently, Tiedemann et al. (1965) have been attempting to detect changes in the RNA of the embryo at the time of neural induction.

A side issue that arose during Toivönen's and Yamada's work needs mention here because it has too often been quoted uncritically and the conclusive experiments have not yet been carried out. Yamada found that heat treatment of liver or bone marrow tissue for times ranging from 25 to 150 sec. altered the regional inducing properties of these tissues. After short heat treatment, the mesoderm-inducing ability was lost; slightly longer treatment led to loss of the hindbrain and spinal cord inductions too, and much longer treatment resulted eventually in loss of forebrain-inducing power as well. The proportions of each type of induction that resulted from Yamada's experiments are shown in Fig. 7.4. It was argued that three qualitatively distinct inducing agents were present, the mesoderm inductor being the most heat-labile and perhaps, therefore, the largest molecule. Certainly it has been shown in the

H

fractionations carried out by Yamada's and Tiedemann's teams that at least two separable factors exist in these tissues and have different inducing properties. It is, however, far from clear what the effect of the heat treatment is: there have been no biochemical investigations of this

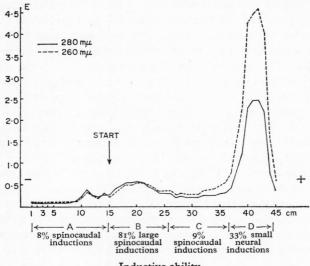

FIG. 7.3 Diagram showing the kinds of induction obtained from different electrophoretic fractions of gastrulae and neurulae. Electrophoresis of MnCl₂ supernatant (about 15 mg protein) after precipitation with ethanol-ether at −20°, solution in 0·2 M sodium phosphate and dialysis against 0·05 M phosphate (pH 7·8). 8 V/cm; 14 h; 0·05 M phosphate (pH 7·8). For analysis at 260 mμ and 280 mμ, 1-cm fractions were eluted. For testing inductive capacity, the eluted fractions were pooled as indicated. (From Tiedemann *et al.*, 1961, by kind permission of the authors.)

problem and it cannot therefore be assumed that any one molecular type is lost or altered while others are unaffected. This is an example of an over-naïve experimental approach, stopping at the biological observation to speculate along the old, familiar lines of controversy instead of carrying on to more difficult, biochemical investigations that would immediately show whether or not the speculations were correct. For a long time in the past, controversy has raged as to whether regional differentiation in the central nervous system is the result of a number of different inducing factors or of differences in concentration of a single factor. In recent years, Toivönen and his followers have accumulated much evidence in support of their theory that *two* factors, a forebrain-inducer and a mesoderm-inducer, interact in different proportions to produce the whole range of regional inductions obtained in normal development (Saxen and Toivönen, 1962). Thought of in terms of bio-

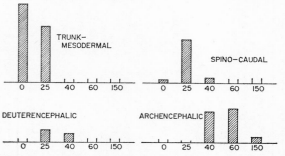

FIG. 7.4 Histograms showing proportions of different types of inductions obtained after heat treatments of from 0 to 150 seconds. (From Yamada, 1958.)

chemical processes, any dichotomy between 'qualitative' and 'quantitative' theories of regional differences in induction seems meaningless: although the differences that eventually appear are qualitative, they are quite likely to have arisen from variations in the numbers of certain identical units, such as enzyme molecules or metabolites. Quantitative differences may quickly lead to qualitative differences: this is usually how we recognize them. As an illustration of this, some of Barth and Barth's data (1963) relating types of induction to the concentration of a single component of a saline medium are quoted in Fig. 7.5.

A final comment needs to be made on these investigations of neural induction by extracts from various adult tissues: this is, that they tell us only the properties of the components extracted from *those particular tissues*. They do *not* prove what components of the embryonic mesoderm are responsible for neural induction in the normal way. Results like those of Tiedemann *indicate* what agents *may* be responsible, but it still

The Effects of Lithium Chloride on the Differentiation of Presumptive Epidermis Cells (Stage II)

Conc., mg/ml	DURATION OF TREATMENT						
	10 min	15–30 min	1 hr	2 hr	4 hr	5 hr	6–9 hr
0·50	Epithelium		Epithelium, nerve	Epithelium Radial nerve Pigment			Pigment
0·75			Nerve, epithelium		Pigment, nerve Epithelium		
1·00	Epithelium	Epithelium	Radial nerve	Spreading nerve Radial nerve	Pigment	Pigment	
1·25	Epithelium	Epithelium	Radial nerve	Spreading nerve Pigment	Pigment, nerve	Pigment	
1·50		Radial nerve	Spreading nerve	Spreading nerve	Pigment, nerve	Pigment	Pigment
2·00	Epithelium		Pigment, nerve	Pigment	Pigment	Pigment	Pigment
2·50			Pigment, nerve		Pigment	Pigment	Pigment
3·00		Nerve	Pigment	Pigment	Pigment	Pigment	
3·50			Radial nerve				
4·00		Radial nerve	Pigment, nerve	Pigment	Pigment		
6·00			Pigment, nerve	Pigment, nerve			

FIG. 7.5 Altered differentiation of ectoderm cells in the presence of various concentrations of lithium chloride. (From Barth and Barth, 1963.)

remains possible that some quite different agents operate in the dorsal lip of the normal embryo. Since the fractions found to be active as neural inductors show certain differences in extracts of different *adult* tissues, it seems even more likely that the active fractions of the embryonic mesoderm are different ones again from these. It is high time these fractionation procedures were used on the isolated 'organizer' tissue itself – or, alternatively, that some quite different approach to the problem was adopted.

In clinching, though unspoken criticism of their own methods, both Toivönen's and Yamada's schools have actually now turned to the other, *in situ* method of investigating neural induction. We shall now consider some of the findings from this type of work, in which components of the intact mesoderm of the gastrula are labelled and then traced into the induced neural plate.

(b) Investigation of induction by labelling and tracer methods

Two main methods have been used to trace material from mesoderm into the induced neural plate. One is to mark the positions of antigens by soaking tissue sections in fluorescent antibody solutions; the other is to label smaller molecules such as nucleotides or amino-acids with radioactive tracers, then to follow their movements in autoradiographs of the sectioned tissues.

The principles, and limitations, of radioactive tracer methods have already been outlined in the previous chapter. The most crucial and difficult matter to decide in interpretations of results is the form in which the tracer has passed into the induced tissue. Radioactivity from an amino-acid of the mesoderm might, for instance, have passed across in the form of protein, peptide, free amino-acid, or indeed in any other metabolite with which the labelled *atoms* of the amino-acid molecule may have exchanged. The same applies to labelled nucleotides. Most of the studies of this kind on induction in amphibians have utilized amino-acid tracers. A very brief summary of these will be sufficient to illustrate the findings and difficulties.

One of the earliest investigators along these lines was Ficq (1954) who soaked frog and salamander gastrulae in 14-C-glycine and then grafted labelled dorsal lip tissue from them into non-radioactive host gastrulae. As a result, the tracer was found to pass into *all* the host tissues – not only into the neural ectoderm. It could not be ascertained in what form the C-14 had passed across – nor, in any case, was it clear to what extent the glycine had been taken up into proteins of the graft beforehand. The later experiments of Sirlin, Brahma, and Waddington (1956) using 35-S-methionine and 14-C-glycine, gave very similar results: so did those of Kuusi (1958), who was utilizing labelled bone marrow as inductor. In all cases, tracer passed into *all* the host tissues, whether they were induced to form neural plate or not, and the form in which the label passed across could not be ascertained. Clearly, much more discriminating methods are needed for these experiments to be useful. One possibility would be to introduce more than one labelled amino-acid (perhaps one tritium-labelled and the other labelled with C-14) into an identifiable protein of the inductor tissue, in known proportions, and then to see if the same protein appeared with the same proportions of tracers in the neural ectoderm. This would provide good evidence that the protein had passed across intact. But it still could not prove, of course, whether this protein was itself a neural inducing agent. A point to be borne in mind is that the concentration of the inducer is probably very low (of the order of 1 : 10,000), and it is not, therefore, the only protein that we see labelled.

Fluorescent antibody labelling procedures do at least discriminate whole antigens rather than much smaller metabolites, and it becomes clear from studies by these methods, that something near a whole protein can pass from inductor into induced neural tissue. Again, however, the entry is not confined to the induced tissue but occurs into other parts of the embryo as well. Flickinger, Hatton, and Rounds (1959) have shown in this way that proteins diagnostic of one species of amphibian can pass across into host tissues of another species. Their finding points up one of the intriguing possibilities revealed by these methods, for it reminds us that the antigen could in some cases simply have been synthesized *in situ* by the host tissues, and not have passed across to them. Sometimes this is unlikely, for the tissues would have to have been induced to synthesize a *foreign* protein. However, it may be clear in cases of the presence of the protein in other tissues too, that it has nothing particular to do with neural differentiation.

Toivönen, Yamada and their collaborators have used fluorescent-antibody-labelling methods on explants. Vainio, Saxen, and Toivönen

(1960) claim to have followed the gradually deeper penetration of recognizable proteins of the bone marrow into the ectoderm cells during the process of induction. Yamada (1962) has found that the yolk platelets are the first site of deposition of antigen passing across from mesoderm or from microsomal fractions of mesoderm into explanted ectoderm sheets floating on nylon. (His method is depicted in Fig. 7.6.) Unfortunately, neither group of workers has yet been able to show conclusively that the proteins which pass across from the inductor have anything at all to do with the process of neural induction.

FIG. 7.6 Culture method used for exposure of gastrula ectoderm for varying times to inducing agents from the mesoderm. (From Yamada and Takata, 1961.) Tissue is placed in a standing-drop culture, on a coverslip (heavy lines), between two pieces of nylon (cross-hatched).

It is appropriate now to look back for a moment to some pioneering work by Niu and Twitty (1953), for they came nearest to answering the crucial question as to *which* of the many substances found to exude from the mesoderm and reach the ectoderm is actually responsible for the process of neural induction. They started with the simple procedure of growing mesoderm cells in hanging-drops of saline and then testing the effects of this 'conditioned' medium on ectoderm explants grown in it. The explants neuralized successfully, and they were also able to show that the conditioned medium contained RNA – perhaps bound to protein. If they pursued this work again, now that more refined ultra-micromethods can be used for the identification of the forms of RNA and of proteins in the mesoderm, they could quite possibly obtain the answer for which we are still waiting. Unfortunately, the partnership ended too soon, and Niu's interest has become diverted to what has proved far more controversial and complex work on the effects of RNA extracted from a number of different adult tissues, including tumours, on the hanging-drop cultures of ectoderm.

It is, of course, cogent to consider whether ideas about specification of proteins by certain new forms of RNA acting as 'messengers' are relevant to the process of neural induction. There is some suggestive evidence (cf. Niu, 1959) about the effects of different forms of RNA on neural ectoderm. Denis (1964) has claimed that induction is suppressed by actinomycin D treatment, which would suppress the synthesis of 'messenger' RNA. It has already been mentioned that Yamada found the higher inducing activity to be in the *ribosomal* fraction from amphibian gastrulae and neurulae. (He did not, it should be noted, isolate the dorsal lip, but only used whole embryos: Yamada, 1960.) His earlier biochemical fractionations had also shown that the active inducing agent in liver was a ribonucleoprotein. Although ribosomes as such cannot pass from one cell into another, the proteins synthesized on them, or alternatively, a more soluble form of RNA could pass across, though the 'messenger' itself might be of too high a molecular weight to do so easily.

In several somewhat imprecise experiments, attempts have been made to judge the molecular size of the inducing agent by interposing filters of known pore size between ectoderm and mesoderm to see whether or not the induction is prevented. Brahma (1958) found, for instance, that neural induction did not take place in Axolotls, *Xenopus*, or *Triturus*, when a membrane of 4 mμ pore size (average) was inserted. Negative results might always imply other adverse effects of the membrane, however. More recently, Saxen (see Saxen and Toivönen, 1962) has found that the neural inducer *can* pass through a membrane of 800 mμ pore size.

It has already been mentioned that specific proteins (antigens) are synthesized in the neural plate before it differentiates visibly (Clayton, 1953). As far as evidence (still only from bacteria with any certainty) goes, two types of cytoplasmic agent could control the synthesis of these specific proteins: messenger RNA itself, or an enzyme inducer (which, according to Jacob and Monod's scheme (Fig. 4.6, p. 63) combines with a cytoplasmic suppressor and thus allows an *m*-RNA synthesis to take place which had otherwise been blocked). The best-known examples of enzyme inducers or suppressors are small metabolites such as amino-acids or low-molecular-weight sugars, which could easily be envisaged to pass across from mesoderm to ectoderm in the embryo: in fact, for amino-acids, we know they do. The difficulty is that there is no known enzyme, specific to neural tissue, which may be identified with the neural induction process. We are back at the point stressed in the introduction to this chapter: our ignorance of what synthesis or other biochemical change is essentially diagnostic of the histological conversion into neural tissue. The only enzyme at all specific to neural tissue is cholinesterase. Unfortunately, however, this particular enzyme has not yet been shown to be inducible in embryos, and it normally does not

(a) SEQUENTIAL INDUCTIONS
    INORGANIC IONS *(Barth and Barth 1963,1964)*

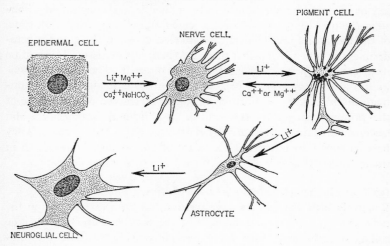

(b) AMINO-ACIDS AS ACTIVATORS

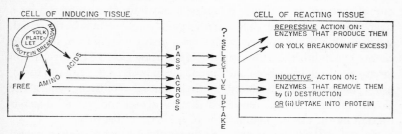

FIG. 7.7 (a) Sequence of differentiation obtained by Barth and Barth in ectoderm cells after culture in saline containing additional magnesium, calcium, or lithium ions. (b) Suggested action of small-molecule inducers passing across from an inducing to a reacting tissue in the early embryo.

appear until much later stages, when synapses are formed between differentiated neurons. So, much as one may wish to draw an analogy between the 'enzyme induction' that is so well known in bacteria and neural induction in embryonic development, there is so far no justification for any such comparison. Recently, however, Wiggert and Villee (1964) have re-emphasized the characteristic differences in esterase pattern and in patterns of isozymes (such as the lactate dehydrogenase series) that are shown by different embryonic tissues of mammals. If any of these enzymes is shown to be inducible, then one might reconsider the possibility that small-molecule inducers may trigger off some of the diagnostic biochemical changes that occur in the gastrula ectoderm at the time when it first turns into neural plate tissue. It would be unwise to carry speculations further at present. The various possibilities already mentioned here have been brought together diagrammatically in Fig. 7.7 *b*. Further light may be thrown on the nature of the protein changes by the studies with lithium, magnesium, and calcium ions pursued recently by Barth and Barth (1963, 1964). They have obtained an interesting sequence of conversions of ectoderm in tissue culture (Fig. 7.7 *a*).

(c) The biochemical basis of neurulation

Relatively little biochemical investigation has been carried out on the next series of events that characterize the neurula stage: namely, the rolling up of the neural tube. It has been noted in observations of respiration rate throughout development that there is a relative slowing of the rate of increase at the time of neural plate formation, followed by a steeper rise (cf. Chap. 10). The essential point would seem to be the initial, steeper rise after the plateau. This presumably results from increased energy expenditure by the neural folds as they close. The mechanical forces involved have been measured, ingeniously, by Selman (1958), using micro-magnets balanced by their mutual repulsion, against the closure of the folds. He estimated that a force of 100×10^{-3} dynes is exerted by the closing neural folds of the Axolotl neurula.

We still do not know what biochemical mechanism causes neural plate cells to contract transversely and produces the folding. Evidence from Ambellan (1958) suggests that an ATPase mechanism like that of muscle may operate. She found that the neurulation process could be speeded up by treating embryos with ATP. Ambellan and Webster (1962) have since shown that di- and mononucleotides are equally effective, but that their efficiency in promoting neurulation is not related to the rate at which they enter the neural plate cells. This subject has not been pursued, and there is a dearth of ideas at the present time about the mechanism of neurulation. We can certainly discard the naïve, older theories involving differential mitosis, or differential inhibition of water on the ventral surface: since there is no evidence to support them. Balinsky (1960 b) also argues against the idea that the outer surfaces of the cells contract, since he has seen folds in these under the electron microscope (cf. Fig. 6.9 and p. 92).

It is only too clear that much remains to be investigated in connexion with the events of neurulation in amphibia. Not only the biochemistry but the energetics, physics, and physiology of this process remain intriguing and unknown. As with investigations on cleavage and gastrulation, one feels the need of some means of slowing down these processes experimentally, to allow time for those delicate manipulations and laborious analyses that have to be applied in order to find out their causes and mechanism.

CHAPTER EIGHT

Events at Tailbud and Hatching Stages

At these terminal stages of embryonic development there is a considerable elongation of the body, brought about chiefly by the development of the tail. The so-called 'tailbud' stage owes its name to the presence of this knob-like mass, or bud, of undifferentiated mesoderm cells, which invaginate behind the rest of the dorsal mesoderm, just after the end of gastrulation. Spofford (1948) pointed out that in some species this tissue looks like a part of the posterior end of the neural plate, before it invaginates and shows itself in reality to be mesodermal. Differentiation of notochord and somites then takes place in this tailbud material, somewhat later than the differentiation of the corresponding trunk tissues.

Many distinctive features of the head region appear at the tailbud stage: the most obvious of these are the eye rudiments, the darkly-pigmented 'sucker' or mucous gland of the mouth region, and protuberances indicating the regions of the brain. In the trunk, divisions between the somites (intersomitic grooves) gradually appear along the dorsolateral surface in craniocaudal sequence. In addition, lateral prominences in the neck and anterior trunk regions mark the gill and kidney rudiments. The contour of the body is at first curved – convex dorsally – but gradually straightens as the tail grows and swings up into line with the dorsal axis (cf. Fig. 2.1, 17–18). Black melanophores begin to appear in the skin, which after hatching becomes remarkably transparent so that many of the internal structures of the head and trunk show through it (Fig. 2.16).

All the features just described are external signs of the phase of *early organogenesis*. We shall discuss in this chapter some of the biochemical events that govern this process, including the precisely co-ordinated cellular activities by which the organs and tissues of the body are initially shaped during the tailbud and early larval stages up to the time of hatching. Both histological and morphological changes are involved in all these re-shaping processes.

(a) The eye

It is appropriate to start with this most prominent and important organ, as a sequel to the account of neural induction in the previous chapter, since the inductive interaction between eye cup and lens has been of interest to investigators for a very long time. In fact, its discovery was the forerunner of the studies on neural induction. The most recent work has been carried out mostly on chick embryos, however, and therefore unfortunately lies outside the scope of this discussion. The two main lines of investigation followed in chick embryos should be mentioned, though, since they serve as models for work that will, one hopes, eventually be carried out on amphibians too. Firstly, the ultrastructure and histochemistry of the zone between eye cup and lens has been studied in some detail in the chick, and the effects on the induction process when filters of various pore sizes are interposed in this zone have been observed (Weiss and Jackson, 1961; McKeehan, 1958). Secondly, the new, adult-type lens proteins that appear in the induced lens have been studied by serological methods (see Maisel and Langman, 1961). α-, β-, and γ-crystallins have been distinguished and appear in this order during embryonic development of the lens. Two of these crystallins, α- and γ-, have also been identified in the lens of adult frogs, but there is no β-crystallin in amphibians.

Amphibian embryos were used in the classical work on lens induction, published by Spemann (1903). In fact, he first evolved his idea that one tissue could influence another's development, with reference to the eye cup and the lens, and it was only later that he applied it to the induction of neural plate by mesoderm. The earliest experiments on lens induction involved extirpation of the eye cup, or alternatively, transplanting it so that it was shown to induce lens-formation by the epidermis of another part of the body. The results of extirpation became somewhat confused later when they were repeated on a number of different species, for it was found that some species were capable of forming a lens in the absence of the eye cup. Later, it was realized that an initial inductive stimulus comes from the dorsal mesoderm underlying the presumptive lens ectoderm before neurulation has started. This stimulus is then supplemented by the action of the eye cup, and the balance between the two factors varies in different species. It may also vary at different temperatures, apparently: for at low temperatures, lens-formation appears less dependent on the eye cup than at higher temperatures (Ten Cate, see Woerdeman, 1939). It has been suggested that this is an example of 'chemodifferentiation' continuing independently of morphological differentiation, so that lens induction takes place at a morphologically earlier stage at low temperature and is already completed by the time there is an eye cup to be extirpated. This, in the author's view, seems neither a likely nor a logical explanation, however, since morphological processes must still depend on the biochemical ones, whatever the temperature. It seems more likely that the earlier reaction results from a more rapid diffusion of the inducing agent through the weakened cell membranes of chilled tissues. The friability of chilled amphibian embryos is most noticeable when one attempts to operate on them.

The nature of the lens-inducing factor in the eye cup is still unknown. Ever since Lopashov (1936) found that eye cups killed by boiling water were still capable of inducing a lens in amphibians, it has been clear that, as in neural induction, we are dealing with a chemical influence and not with any property of living inductor cells. De Vincentiis (1954) found that lens induction was prevented by inserting a filter between eye cup and lens in the frog embryo. This suggests that a high-molecular-weight inductor is involved. The inductor in the eye cup is not assumed to be the same as the mesodermal factor responsible for the initial stimulus, however. It seems likely that the mesodermal factor is part of the neural inducing system: if so, it may be a ribonucleoprotein. It is particularly interesting that some workers, notably Becker (1959) have obtained inductions of 'free' lenses, with no eye cup, after implanting various foreign neural inducing agents in amphibians. Such findings strongly suggest identity between the neural and the lens-inducing factors. Becker has not so far discovered the biochemical nature of the free lens inductor, however. So we still have to admit complete ignorance of the agent responsible for lens induction in amphibians. No light has been thrown on this problem by histochemical studies, either. Claims that RNA 'passes across' from eye cup to lens have not been properly substantiated and it seems wisest to interpret them as indicating a rapid synthesis of RNA in the induced tissue, which is certainly to be expected when it is forming new proteins.

Even while it is still only at the placode stage, the lens rudiment starts to form specific lens proteins, recognizable by serological methods (Ten Cate and van Doorenmaalen, 1950). The sequence of appearance of these antigens was first followed by Flickinger and Stone (1960) and by Langman and Prescott (1959). Since then, Ogawa (1965) and Smith (1965), using improved immunological and electrophoretic methods, have distinguished the embryonic lens proteins, some of which are a first present in other tissues as well, but lost later. Usually seven or eight antigens, confined to the lens placode, can be distinguished and two or three of these are identical with adult lens antigens. It is interesting to note also that the iris, which is capable of regenerating a lens after the normal one has been extirpated (Stone, 1950), has antigens in common with the normal lens. Ogawa (1964) has shown that the regenerated lens, formed from the iris, is destroyed by specific lens antibodies in just the same way as is the normal lens. The proteins of the rest of the eye cup have not been studied in any detail. Mezger-Fried and Oppenheimer (1965) have observed changes in the RNA of the developing eye cup and lens, however, which may be associated with the formation of new ribosomes.

It is well known that the lens can itself influence the later growth of the eye cup. This has been shown in experiments in which lenses were grafted between species of different sizes, or between individuals of the same species at different ages (see Twitty, 1955). Both eye cup and lens accommodate their growth rate to adapt to each other's size, in these cases. It is not known what factors control this mutual adjustment, however: differing metabolic rates have been suggested, but there is a need for biochemical work on this problem.

Within the retina, neural and pigment layers are to some extent modifiable and may be influenced by adjacent organs such as the ear vesicle (Dragomirow, 1936). Extra neural retina may form instead of the pigment layer, at the point where a grafted ear vesicle makes contact. The same graft may induce additional lens fibres if it makes contact with the developing lens, however. Its stimulus appears, therefore, to be quite non-specific, like the stimulus of thyroxin at metamorphosis (cf. Chapter Nine). It is the tissues themselves, and not the inducer, that contain information making them react in specific ways.

It is unknown what factors initiate melanin synthesis in the pigment layer of the retina. One may surmise, however, by analogy with the needs of neural crest cells (see below), that adequate supplies of phenyl-alanine and/or tyrosine are essential.

(b) The neural crest

The cells of this tissue have long attracted investigators owing to their remarkable motility, their versatile power of differentiation (cf. Chapter

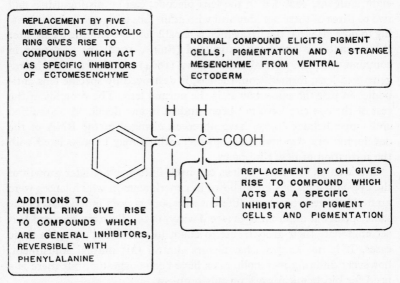

FIG. 8.1 Effects of different analogues of phenylalanine on the differentiation of amphibian neural crest cells. (Wilde, 1955.)

Two) and the ready identifiability of those that form melanophores. Incidentally, it has been shown recently that pterins also are synthesized in melanophores (Hama and Obika, 1960: Obika, 1963). But by far the major component of their pigment is melanin.

Wilde (1955, 1956) aroused much interest by his investigations of the role of phenylalanine in neural crest differentiation. He claimed to be able to convert ventral epidermis into neural crest, by growing it in a hanging-drop culture to which phenylalanine had been added. Conversely, he found that the differentiation of the neural crest was inhibited by analogues of phenylalanine. Further, it appeared that the type of analogue used governed the type of differentiation that was inhibited (Fig. 8.1). In later experiments, Wilde added precursors of phenylalanine to see whether they reversed the effects of the inhibitors.

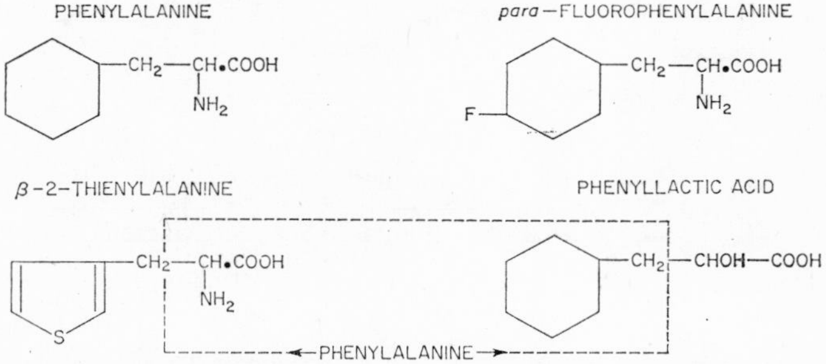

FIG. 8.2 Possible synthesis of phenylalanine from components of two of its analogues. (Wilde, 1956.)

He found that if archenteron roof mesoderm was also present, these precursors had the same effect on ventral epidermis as had normal phenylalanine, but in the absence of mesoderm there was no effect. He concluded that the archenteron roof mesoderm was able to synthesize phenylalanine from the precursors (cf. Fig. 8.2) and to transfer it to the ectoderm. This interesting idea could easily be tested by labelling the mesoderm with radioactive precursors, or alternatively, with radioactive phenylalanine to show whether this amino-acid is normally transferred from the archenteron roof to the neural crest. Unfortunately, this test has not been done, however, and Wilde appears to have lost interest in the problem. It is one of general importance, nevertheless, for it is quite plausible on current views of enzyme induction to imagine a small metabolite such as an amino-acid acting as inductor of neural crest. Phenylalanine might, for instance, induce phenylalanine hydroxylase activity and thus initiate melanin synthesis via tyrosine (Fig. 8.3).

In a number of studies on neural crest cells *in vitro*, Twitty and Niu

I

(1948) observed that they repel each other, apparently by some chemical means. This could account for their migratory behaviour in the embryo. One cell alone in a capillary tube remains immobile, but as soon as another cell is introduced, the two move away from each other. Larger groups of cells disperse at rates related to the density of the population and the volume of medium. Dalton and Hall (see Dalton, 1953) compared the behaviour of melanophores from white and black axolotls,

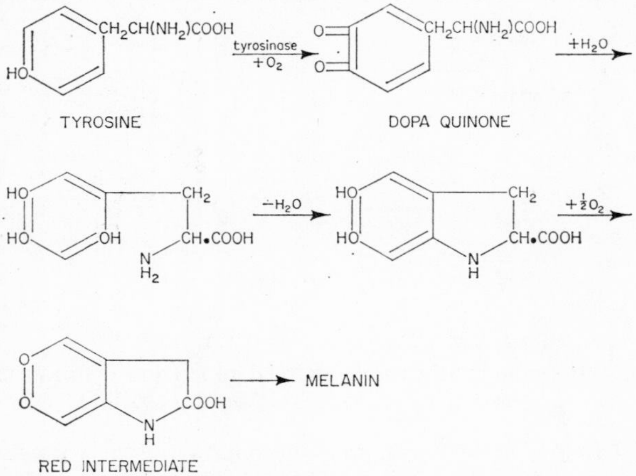

FIG. 8.3 Scheme of the steps towards melanin synthesis.

which differ by a single gene mutation (whites are dd, double recessive; blacks either heterozygous Dd or homozygous dominant DD). Both types of melanophore migrate, and synthesize melanin, equally well *in vitro*. The difference in pigmentation in the animals is entirely due to an inhibition of migration of the melanophores by the white-type skin. Dalton showed this clearly by skin grafts at stages before the neural crest cells had started to migrate. It is the epidermis, then, and not the neural crest that differs in the two types. The biochemistry of this difference awaits investigation.

Many other fascinating problems are posed for the investigator by these versatile neural crest cells. There must, for instance, be moments, and places, at which their metabolism must 'hang in the balance' between two quite different courses of differentiation. An interesting and puzzling feature is that only *head* neural crest cells, and not those derived from the trunk, will form cartilage (Newth, 1954). We have here a good example of the fact that some last-minute switch in metabolism may decide the fate of a cell. If it lies at the borderline between head and trunk it might turn it into either a chondroblast or a melanoblast. In the spinal cord region, some cells become Schwann cells and synthesize myelin, while others become ganglion cells or mesenchymal cells. Clearly it requires something more complex than an interplay of phenylalanine precursors to account for these diverse pathways of development.

(c) The peripheral nervous system

The chief events of the development of the nervous system at tailbud and early larval stages (cf. Chapter Two) are the differentiation of neuroblasts into neurons and the outgrowth of fibres from these to reach specific end-organs. It has been shown by Hughes and Tschumi (1958) that the numbers of motor as well as sensory neuroblasts that differentiate into neurons is modifiable by peripheral stimuli. When the development or regeneration of a limb is suppressed, the numbers of both sensory and motor neurons are reduced. So far, the biochemical basis of this control is unknown. We also know very little, despite numerous experiments, of the factors that control the direction of outgrowth of nerve fibres in the embryo. In some important experiments, Levi-Montalcini (1958, 1964) and Cohen (1958) showed that phenylalanine and also a protein that was originally extracted from snake venom but is found in various sera too, stimulate fibre outgrowth from chick sensory ganglia. Neither agent exerts any influence on the *direction* of the fibres' growth, however. Weiss (see 1955 a) has shown quite convincingly that mechanical factors guide the outgrowth of nerve fibres in tissue culture. But it is difficult to envisage how any such mechanical factors could operate in the embryo which has not yet developed any connective tissue: it seems much more likely that the factors operating are chemical ones, though there is no evidence yet from *in vivo* experiments to demonstrate this conclusively. We still have no biochemical explanation to offer for the fact that, when a limb bud is transplanted a few segments further posterior, its proper spinal nerves will deviate their course to innervate it in its new position.

In describing the early differentiation of the nervous system (Chapter

Two) a few special cells peculiar to amphibians and fish were mentioned. Of these, Mauthner's cells are specially suitable for biochemical investigations owing to their large size. It is interesting that in haploids, the mechanism that decides which two hindbrain cells shall become these giant neurons is apparently upset and there may be four neurons

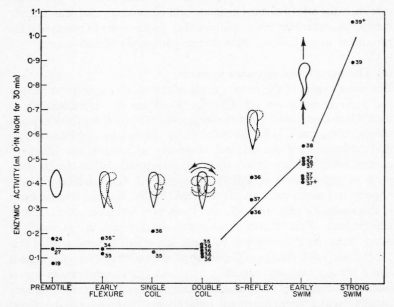

FIG. 8.4 The development of cholinesterase activity and of motile behaviour in the salamander, *Ambystoma punctatum*. Ordinate denotes enzyme activity: abscissa, sequence of behaviour manifestations. (Sawyer, 1943: reproduced from Boell, 1955, by kind permission.)

instead of two (Weiss, 1955). At least one biochemical peculiarity of these cells is known, in goldfish: they have an RNA base composition quite unlike that of the spinal cord cells (Edström *et al.*, 1962). In amphibians these cells have not yet been analysed, but are likely to have special properties too.

At the late tailbud stage, the earliest 'behaviour' may be said to begin. A muscular twitching, at first myogenic, becomes governed by reflex arcs as soon as these are complete. Connected with this motility, cholinesterase activity appears. The course of this enzyme activity through amphibian development was first investigated by Sawyer (1943), whose results are shown graphically in Fig. 8.4, and has since been followed in more detail by Boell, Greenfield, and Shen (1955). There is a rapid rise of cholinesterase activity just before hatching, when movements become vigorous. Besides biochemical methods, Boell and Shen used a histochemical test in order to locate the sites of first appearance of cholinesterase activity in developing amphibians, and found that it was localized very clearly in developing synapse zones.

(d) The muscular system

The early muscle cells (myoblasts) begin to differentiate after the somite mesoderm has segmented into blocks (cf. Chapter Two). The process of segmentation itself raises biochemical problems, mainly unanswered so far. A little speculation about these is justifiable, in order to emphasize the problems that require further investigation. One may first ask how the spacing and number of the divisions between the somites are controlled. Waddington and Deuchar (1953) suggested a rhythmical system governed by the interaction of two or more chemical processes. These could perhaps originate from a random flux of materials such as Turing (1952) envisaged. Turing's theory, however, referred to an originally circular or spherical group of cells: it is not readily applicable to a sheet of cells like the archenteron roof. The problem, then, is to think of a biochemical process that determines proportionate sizes of cell groups, according to the total number of cells present, in such a way that the total number of groups remains constant. For in amphibian embryos, neither the shape nor the number of somites is altered by addition or removal of pieces of archenteron roof before segmentation has started: only the size of the individual somites is modified in these experiments. Figure 8.5 represents a hypothesis of the present author, which attempts to account for this size and shape control in the somite cells. It is undoubtedly far too simple, but may stimulate others to devise more plausible schemes or at least to think of experiments to test this one.

The particular emphasis of Fig. 8.5 is on the changes in shape and adhesive behaviour of the somite cells. These cells, like the gastrula cells described earlier (Chapter Six), evidently show selective adhesion when

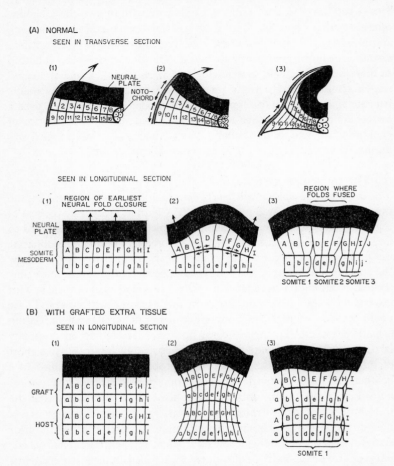

FIG. 8.5 Diagram to illustrate how the sequence of deformation in the neural plate during neurulation could bring about changes in shape of the archenteron roof cells, resulting in their segregation into somites whose length and height are interdependent. Cells are numbered or lettered, for identification of their supposed changes inposition. Stage (1) early neurula; stage (2) mid-neurula; stage (3) late neurula.

they become rearranged into rosettes, losing adhesion to cells of the adjacent somite and at the same time adhering more extensively to the cells of their own somite. The basis of this behaviour is not known, but there is a little evidence that the initial adhesions and movements may depend on myosin-like ATPase activity (Deuchar, 1961 *a*). In the presence of ATP, disaggregated somite cells reaggregate more quickly than do controls. Moreover, ATP speeds up the rate of somite segmentation in isolated dorsal halves of embryos. It has similar effects on chick embryos (Deuchar, 1960 *a* and *b*). ATPase activity is also enhanced by the ATP treatment.

Another metabolite that appears to affect the differentiation of somites, in chick embryos at least, is leucine: addition of it to a culture medium will increase the rate of somite-formation. Conversely, analogues of leucine may block somite segmentation (Herrmann, 1953). These phenomena are not demonstrable in *Xenopus* embryos, however, presumably because all necessary supplies of leucine can be obtained from the intracellular yolk and the addition of extraneous leucine or analogues therefore makes little difference. It has been observed, however, that there is a high concentration of free leucine in dorsal regions of the late neurula of *Xenopus*, which decreases at the tailbud stage when the somites start to segment. There is also at this time a much higher leucine-activation in somite mesoderm than in other dorsal tissues (Deuchar, 1961 *b*, 1962). All this suggests that leucine is taken up particularly rapidly into protein of the somite cells at this time. A possible reason for this rapid uptake is that the myoblasts are synthesizing myosin, which contains a relatively high percentage (about 10%) of leucine (Block and Weiss, 1956).

Ogawa (1961) has identified myosin in frog embryos by serological methods. He finds that its appearance is normally preceded by that of actin, but myosin is not prevented from forming if the synthesis of actin is experimentally blocked.

(e) Sclerotome and dermatome

These two parts of the somite have one biochemical feature in common: they both synthesize collagen at an early stage of development. Autoradiographic work on the uptake of tritium-labelled proline suggests that the earliest site of accumulation of collagen precursors is in the notochord sheath and the sclerotome cells that come to surround it. Fig. 8.6 gives some of the results (Deuchar, 1964). A little later, radioactivity appears in the dermis (derived from dermatome). There is

From Grain Counts on Autoradiographs of Tailbud Stage Embryos

(Data are mean numbers of grains per 144 sq. μ, $\pm$ standard errors)

Neural tube	*Chorda*	*Sclerotome*	*Dermatome*
49·8 ± 2·8	69·9 ± 3·8	57·2 ± 2·1	56·6 ± 2·3

Myotome	*Lateral mesoderm*	*Endoderm*	*Ventral epidermis*
32·4 ± 2·5	32·7 ± 1·6	22·4 ± 3·3	49·5 ± 3·4

FIG. 8.6 Uptake of tritium-labelled proline into tissues of tailbud-stage embryos of *Xenopus laevis*. (Deuchar, 1964.)

evidence of radioactivity in protein-bound hydroxyproline (diagnostic of collagen) from analyses of hydrolysates at quite early embryonic stages (Fig. 8.7), but labelled hydroxyproline does not appear in the insoluble protein fraction until three days after hatching. This suggests

	Proline	Hydroxy-proline	Glycine	Other amino-acids
Fertilized egg	137	24	0	91
Cleavage stages	107	32	0	197
Blastula	278	22	0	81
Gastrula	65	23	0	83
Neurula	47	0	0	42
Tailbud	206	0	0	44
Hatching	540	38	30	78
1-day larva	262	21	0	34
3-day larva	31	98	0	10

FIG. 8.7 Protein-bound radioactivity in *Xenopus laevis* embryos, labelled with tritiated proline at the oocyte stage. Counts/min/μg protein.

that collagen precursors are synthesized quite early in embryonic development, but are not converted into stable, insoluble collagen until the 3-day larval stage.

(f) The tail and its differentiation

Before going on to deal with events after the tailbud stage, a word should be said about the tailbud itself, which is peculiar in the lateness of its differentiation compared with other parts of the body. It has been mentioned already that the tailbud mesoderm is derived from involuted material which, to all appearances, was originally part of the neural plate. Yet at a late stage, it is induced instead to form mesoderm. It would be most interesting to know if the factor responsible for this mesodermal induction, which presumably emanates from posterior archenteron roof cells, is at all like the mesoderm-inducing protein that Yamada isolated from bone marrow (cf. Chapter Seven).

Among the very few properties of the tailbud that have been noted is its catheptic activity (Urbani, 1955) which is higher than in other regions of the embryo at this stage. One is led to wonder whether this is due to late yolk breakdown, or whether the conversion from apparent neural plate to an apparently undifferentiated mesodermal mass has involved the breakdown of some proteins characteristic of neural tissue.

Recently Briggs *et al.* (1964) have demonstrated by nuclear transfer experiments that of all nuclear types at late developmental stages, tailbud cell nuclei produce the highest percentage of successful development in enucleated eggs. This seems to confirm the idea that the tailbud is relatively undifferentiated. Gurdon (1960) obtained only 4% successful development with gut cells of young *Xenopus* larvae. One may comment that although these gut cells are still full of yolk until late in larval life, they already possess some form of intrinsic differentiation. Isolation and transplantation experiments indicate that they are already determined as to the parts of the gut they will form, in gastrula and neurula stages.

(g) The gut and viscera

The metabolism of the gut cells must be adjusted at a later stage than other cells of the late embryo and larva to the task of breaking down yolk on a large scale. The breakdown products can be transported to other cells of the body when the blood circulation develops. Blood cells form first from mesoderm of the flank and hind trunk region of the young larva. The haemoglobin synthesized in these cells is different from adult haemoglobin and is replaced at metamorphosis by the adult form (cf. Chapter Nine). Tooze and Davies (1963) have described the early synthesis of haemoglobin in these blood cells. Further features of the development of internal organs in the larva will be dealt with in

Chapter Nine, and the brief remarks in the present chapter refer only to changes that are initiated before hatching.

(h) Hatching

As already mentioned in Chapter Two, hatching is effected not only mechanically by wriggling movements, but also by enzymatic breakdown of the jelly capsule. Experiments using radioactive sodium as tracer (Dainty, Deuchar and Oliver, 1952, unpublished) show that contents of the capsule enter the gut during this process. The hatching enzymes of amphibians have not been identified so far, though some are known and characterized in fish (Kaighn, 1964).

(i) Conclusion

It is only too clear that our information on the biochemical processes that govern early tissue differentiation in amphibian embryos is very incomplete. The dearth of investigations on these forms does not arise from the fact that they are amphibians, but because they are embryos, whose enormous disadvantage to biochemists is their minute size. If research in this field is to make any headway, it must become a collaborative effort between biologists, willing to isolate large quantities of tissues for analysis, and biochemists, keen with new ultramicromethods for such analyses and able to pursue the biochemical implications of the biologists' naïve and ingenuous experiments on cause and effect in development.

Developmental Processes in the Larva and at the Time of Metamorphosis

The development of any animal from egg to adult involves a prolonged period of growth, usually following after the major processes of differentiation of organs and tissues are complete. In amphibians, this growth phase occurs during larval life. Some differentiation processes also continue in the larva until specialized organs such as the fins, balancers, gills, mouth parts, and gut, which are still only rudimentary at the time of hatching, are fully formed. Very few of these finer details of differentiation have been investigated biochemically, partly because they are on such a small scale that investigation would be difficult. But the cells also retain an ability to undergo very large-scale alterations: this is evidenced by the two remarkable phenomena of regeneration and metamorphosis, which will be discussed more fully below. But first, as a corrective to the biochemists' tendency to regard growing animals as just another kind of 'bulk material', some mention will be made of the small-scale changes of larval development, which are also of considerable interest and importance.

(a) General features of larval development
The larva differs from the embryo in being free-swimming, independent of yolk as main source of nutriment, and proof against the foreign physico-chemical features of the environment without the protection of a jelly capsule. All these characteristics are acquired gradually. The free-swimming habit is usually attained only after a preliminary stage when the larva is mostly immobile, hanging vertically from protective surfaces such as the leaves of water plants. Effective swimming, including the rapid, darting movements characteristic of the escape reaction, is

achieved only after full development of the longitudinal fibre tracts in the spinal cord, as well as the reflex arcs in each segment. Mauthner's neurons (p. 25) figure prominently in the control of rapid movements, and if these giant cells are removed surgically (Detwiler, 1933) the larva is lethargic.

The larva cannot be said to have attained full independence of the yolk until the considerable quantity remaining in the gut cells has been absorbed. Besides probably contributing to the proteins of these cells, yolk products are later distributed via the blood stream from the gut to other tissues of the body. The phase of yolk absorption is characterized by a steeply increasing cathepsin activity (Urbani, 1955; Vecchioli, 1956). It is not completed until two or three weeks after hatching in most forms, i.e. not until a long time after the larva has begun to feed. During this period, and partly as a result of the concomitant differentiation of the viscera, the ventral parts of the body become more resistant to mechanical damage and also to bacterial infections which at stages just after hatching are most liable to attack the ventral regions. Before hatching the jelly affords protection against invasions by bacteria, fungi, and protozoa: it also gives mechanical protection. In addition, the jelly acts as an osmotic barrier: immediately after hatching it is quite common, particularly in *Xenopus laevis*, for waterlogging of the tissues to occur and for subepidermal 'blisters' to form, whenever any abnormality of development has impaired the function of the kidney. In normal circumstances, the pronephric kidney begins to function very shortly after hatching and excretes water to counteract the tendency to endosmosis (Fox, 1963).

One of the most striking features of larval development is the great increase in body size, which is of course dependent on an adequate food supply as well as being controlled by growth hormones from the pituitary. During this growth the tail becomes considerably longer than the trunk, in most species, and its fin broadens. It acquires an increasingly complex pattern of pigmentation, characteristic for the species, as many transplantation experiments have shown. Pigment cells (neural crest) transplanted from another species distribute themselves in the host according to the pattern of the donor species: in other words, their genetic characteristics govern how and where they migrate. It has already been pointed out (p. 120), however, that in white axolotls it is the character of the epidermis, and not of the melanophores themselves, that govern their sparse distribution in the skin. The white-type skin inhibits melanophore migration. Wilde (1960) has given a useful review of experimental work on pigmentation and melanophore development in vertebrates, to which the interested reader may refer for a fuller account of this very attractive subject.

A special organ of the skin in the mouth region is the larval *sucker*, characteristic of Anurans and varying considerably in structure in different species. Eakin (1963) has described the ultrastructure of the larval sucker in the treefrog, *Hyla regilla*. He has also found that its differentiation was inhibited by treatment of the neurula stage with actinomycin D (Eakin, 1964).

The remaining events of larval differentiation and growth all ultimately lead to the much more dramatic and accelerated changes of metamorphosis. Only the intestine and pancreas are, like the gills and the Anuran tail, destined to be lost. All the other organ systems continue to grow and differentiate after metamorphosis and on into adult life. The nervous system increases in complexity of fine detail. The eye acquires further, iridescent pigment in its choroid layer and its cornea becomes transparent. The visual pigment in the larval retina – porphyropsin, a derivative of Vitamin A_2 – becomes replaced by rhodopsin, derived by a different metabolic pathway from Vitamin A_1, at metamorphosis (see p. 137). The musculature of the head and trunk continues to increase in bulk, the individual myoblasts becoming fused into bundles and acquiring cross-striations. The skeleton continues to lay down cartilage during larval life, but very little ossification takes place until the time of metamorphosis. The heart and blood vessels complete their finer details of form and distribution, and blood cells are continuously produced in the liver at first, then later in the spleen when it develops. The major endocrine glands – pituitary and thyroid – as well as the thymus, ultimobranchial body and parathyroids, develop and, as far as we know, control the growth of tissues much as they do in the adult animal, until metamorphosis. Flickinger (1964) has found that both the head and lower jaw regions of *Rana pipiens* at the tailbud stage are already able to synthesize mono-iodotyrosine. Both mono- and di-iodotyrosine are formed in the thyroid of the 11 mm larva and thyroxine is also present here by the 16 mm stage. No tissues of the *Rana* larva other than the thyroid are able to concentrate iodine (Flickinger, 1963).

We shall now go on to consider the highly specialized process of metamorphosis in more detail.

(b) Metamorphosis

(i) External features and inductive interactions

Bennett and Frieden (1962) have reviewed the main biochemical changes that occur during amphibian metamorphosis: the following account will deal with these more selectively and with additional references to more recent findings.

It has been known since the early part of this century that the onset of metamorphosis in amphibians is brought about by the action of the thyroid hormone. We are still far from understanding the biochemical basis of this hormone's action on the many different tissues involved in the metamorphic changes, however. Some tissues also interact secondarily with each other, so that the whole situation is quite complex.

The first sign of impending metamorphosis is the emergence of the hind limbs. Much later, when these are well developed, the forelimbs also appear, having developed within the gill chamber and then pushed their way out through either the operculum or a region of degenerating skin (cf. Fig. 2.16). One of the earliest observations of an inductive interaction here was made by Helff (1928). He noted that the degenerating gill tissue caused thinning and perforation of the skin overlying it, thus facilitating the emergence of the forelimb. If the gill tissue was transplanted elsewhere, it caused the same changes in the skin that lay over at any other point in the body. The factor acting on the skin is believed to be some protein degradation product from the gills, but no attempt has yet been made to isolate it or to characterize it biochemically.

In the development of the limb-buds themselves, there is a complex interaction between mesoderm and ectoderm. The thickened 'apical ridge' of ectoderm (also seen, rather more strikingly, in the limb-buds of bird and mammal embryos) is essential for the formation of distal parts of the limb. Without it, no digits will form (Tschumi, 1956). This ridge depends on the mesoderm, however, for its maintenance and proper growth. The ectoderm-mesoderm interactions have been worked out in more detail in birds (see Zwilling, 1960, for review). Tschumi (loc. cit.) demonstrated similar properties in the apical limb ectoderm of *Xenopus laevis*.

Associated with the changes in the pharynx and forelimb regions is the development of the tympanic membrane (ear-drum). This, in amphibians, is induced to form by the presence of the columella cartilage beneath it, as well as by the tympanic cartilage. (The columella is the only ear 'ossicle' in amphibians.) In the absence of these cartilages, no ear-drum forms, or if either of them is transplanted, it induces an ear-drum to form in whatever skin now overlies it.

Further changes at metamorphosis in Anurans are the characteristic protrusion of the eyes and, most obvious and cataclysmic event, the complete resorption of the tail which presents an immediate, striking problem to both morphologists and biochemists alike. Why should the tail *regress* in response to thyroxin, while other organs are stimulated to develop, by the same hormone? Schwind (1933) showed that if the eye was transplanted to the tail, it showed no signs whatever of degeneration although it remained firmly attached to the regressing tail all through metamorphosis. So the eye was completely uninfluenced by the tissues of the tail. Both eye and tail respond independently, in different ways, to the stimulus of the same hormone. This shows very clearly that thyroxin operates a quite non-specific stimulus and is in no sense a carrier of 'information' or 'instructions' to the tissues: they must carry these within themselves.

(ii) Internal features of metamorphosis: atrophy, hypertrophy and change
The most obvious of the internal changes is the development of lungs, which replace the gills and supplement the skin as adult respiratory organs. Associated with the new respiratory circulation are modifications of the pharyngeal blood vessels. These will not be detailed here – the essentials are illustrated in Fig. 9.1. Like other blood vessel alterations, they are preceded and to some extent controlled by changes in the rate of blood flow (Hughes, 1937). The heart, too, modifies to accommodate the increased volume of blood returned from the lungs, and the left auricle enlarges to an extent that differs in different species according to the size and importance of the lungs. This is an example of the well-known tendency for growing organs to modify their size

according to physiological conditions. The disappearance, or 'atrophy', of certain organs such as the notochord, the gills and the pronephric kidney may be the result of physiological stimuli. Fox (1957) has shown that the pronephros is also capable of *compensatory hypertrophy* in young newt larvae, after experimental blockage of the pronephric duct on one side of the body. There have been many attempts to explain the causes of compensatory hypertrophy. Widest publicity has been given to Weiss's idea (1955 *b*) that each tissue produces specific extracellular

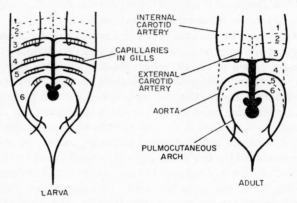

FIG. 9.1 Diagram of the aortic vessels in an amphibian, before and after metamorphosis (after Grove and Newell, 1944).

growth-inhibitors (antitemplates). When any damage or other adverse event reduces the concentration of specific antitemplates that are in circulation in the body, growth of the contralateral organ is supposed to be less inhibited and so to increase, until the antitemplate concentration is brought up to normal and growth is once more inhibited. There appear to be no other known instances of compensatory hypertrophy in embryonic or larval tissues. Weiss's theory is of special interest to embryologists, however, since somewhat similar ideas have been put forward to explain how the lymphatic system of the embryo learns to recognize 'self' from 'non-self', and its resultant lack of immune reaction to its own tissues or to any tissue with which it has been exposed (e.g. by a grafting experiment) during embryonic life (Billingham, Brent, and Medawar, 1956). It has been postulated, for instance, that each cell-type in the

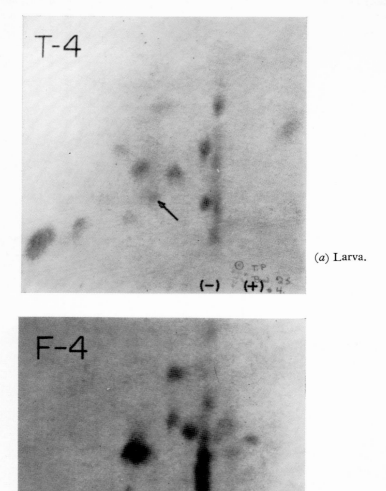

(a) Larva.

(b) Adult.

FIG. 9.2 Patterns of peptides obtained from haemoglobin of larval and adult *Rana pipiens*. (From Baglioni and Sparks, 1963, by kind permission of the authors.)

embryo secretes an extracellular antigen (template) that stimulates certain of the lymphocytes to produce a specific antibody (antitemplate) to it. It has then been argued either that the antitemplate is 'remembered' by the lymphocytes as a result of this reaction or, according to the 'clonal selection theory' of Burnet (1956), that the lymphocyte is killed, leaving only non-reactors as survivors to contribute to the embryo's developing immune system. Recently Haurowitz (1965) has produced new arguments in favour of the template theory and against Burnet's 'clonal selection' theory.

These theories are virtually irrefutable at present, for it would be extremely difficult to prove that *no* such antigen templates were produced by embryonic cells. But there is also, so far, no precise evidence to support them. They still provide stimulating bases for thinking and discussion, however – this is their chief attraction and merit.

Radical *changes of form* occur in the *gut* at metamorphosis. These are apparently related to the change from a herbivorous diet to a carnivorous one, but exactly how this relationship works is unknown. The morphological changes precede the change of diet, so they must be inherent in the genetic mechanism that governs the response of the cells to thyroxin at this stage. One particularly interesting point is that the pancreas is entirely remodelled, after degenerating completely, with the islet tissue as well. This occurs between stages 59 and 66 in *Xenopus* (see Nieuwkoop and Faber, 1956). The functioning of the newly-formed pancreas is associated with a switch over to adult-type glycogen metabolism (Beaumont, 1954) and the liver begins to store glycogen at this stage. Nothing is known of the changes in enzyme activity relevant to glycogen metabolism, however. Tata (pers. comm., 1964) has, however, used the well established increases in activity of urea-cycle enzymes (see below, Fig. 9.6) as a convenient time scale for assessing the rate of metamorphosis in *Rana catesbeiana*. It is interesting that after metamorphosis, tryptophan peroxidase activity may be induced in the liver by tryptophan treatment (Spiegel and Spiegel, 1964). These authors were unable to induce the enzyme activity prior to metamorphosis, and could not confirm Stearns and Kostellow's report (see p. 94) that it could be induced in gastrula endoderm cells.

The new insulin synthesized in the newly-formed pancreas at metamorphosis offers a very interesting subject for future investigation. If

K

the structure of the insulin molecule differs at different stages of amphibian development insulin may, like other proteins such as haemoglobin and lactate dehydrogenase, have a 'molecular embryology' worth studying at the same time as the embryogenesis of the cells in which it is secreted.

Two special molecular changes have been followed through the metamorphosis period in frogs: the changes in haemoglobin and those

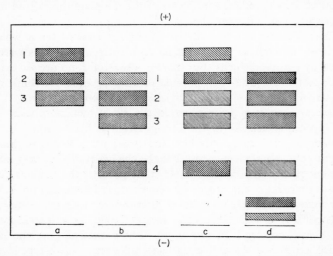

FIG. 9.3 Diagram of the starch-gel electrophoresis pattern of haemoglobin of (a) tadpoles; (b) frogs; (c) metamorphosing tadpoles, and (d) older frogs. (Baglioni and Sparks, 1963.)

in the visual pigment. Baglioni and Sparks (1963) noted that at the time of metamorphosis both larval and adult types of haemoglobin (distinguishable electrophoretically) are present simultaneously. The larval types disappear as the production of erythrocytes is gradually taken over by the bone marrow in the adult frog. Baglioni and Sparks identified peptide differences between these haemoglobins (Fig. 9.2) and it is interesting to note that the adult peptide pattern is more complex, with a wider variety of peptides represented than in the larval haemoglobin. There are also more –SH groups in the adult form of haemoglobin. Two polypeptides can be separated by electrophoresis from each of the globins (Fig. 9.3), and those of the adult frog show slower-moving components than three out of four of the tadpole globins, suggesting larger molecular size in the adult forms. An interesting physiological feature of the larval haemoglobin is that its oxygen-binding powers are independent of pH, whereas the oxygen-binding of adult haemoglobin is pH-dependent. This suggests that the larval form of haemoglobin is an 'adaptation' to the vicissitudes of aquatic life. We still know very little of the physiology of oxygen transport in various forms of amphibians, however. Recently, Boell, Greenfield, and Hille (1963) have found that the gills can be removed from axolotl larvae without impairment of oxygen uptake unless the level of oxygen saturation is extremely

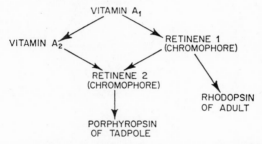

FIG. 9.4 Scheme of the alternative pathways of visual pigment synthesis. (After Ohtsu, Naito, and Wilt, 1964, by kind permission of the authors.)

low (5%). They doubt whether the haemoglobin in this species plays any essential role in oxygen transport. But there is no doubt of its role in the Anurans studied.

Ohtsu, Naito, and Wilt (1964) have studied the synthesis of visual pigment in response to thyroxin at metamorphosis in *Rana catesbeiana*. Before metamorphosis the tadpoles convert Vitamin A.1 to retinene 2, a precursor of the visual pigment, porphyropsin (Fig. 9.4). During metamorphosis the ability to convert A.1 to A.2 and retinene 1 to retinene 2 is lost. Thus retinene 1 becomes the pigment precursor ('chromophore') and gives rise to rhodopsin, the adult visual pigment. This change, it is worth noting, involves a loss, not a gain, of a metabolic step, which is perhaps due to loss of the enzyme activity catalysing this step. Wilt has been able to elicit this same pigment change in organ cultures of eyes and thus to show that it occurs in direct response to thyroxin treatment (cf. Weber's and Shaffer's results with isolated tails, p. 141).

A more generalized biochemical change that is also under the control of thyroxin and occurs at the onset of metamorphosis is the conversion

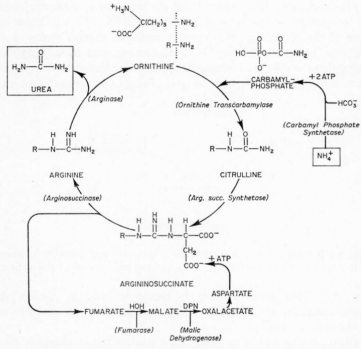

FIG. 9.5 Scheme of urea cycle and its enzymes. (From Bennett and Frieden, 1962.)

of ammonia into urea. In neotenous amphibians such as the axolotl, ammonia remains the main component (about 50%) of the urine, but at metamorphosis in forms that emerge on to land, there is a reduction of the ammonia to some 25% of the urine, while the proportion of urea increases. It is interesting that *Xenopus*, which is aquatic all its life, does not excrete such a high proportion of urea as other adult Anurans

(Munro, 1939). Brown and Cohen (1958) have measured the carbamyl phosphate synthetase activity in various amphibian species, finding that this corresponds to their urea-synthesizing ability and usually increases greatly at metamorphosis. They have also noted an increase in arginase activity in the liver at metamorphosis. The relationship of these enzymes to the urea cycle is shown in Fig. 9.5, and their increase during metamorphosis is depicted in Fig. 9.6.

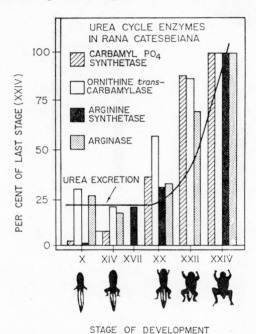

FIG. 9.6 Increases in enzyme activities during metamorphosis in *Rana catesbeiana*. (From Bennett and Frieden, 1962.)

(iii) The hormonal control of metamorphosis
Full accounts of the experiments that established the relationship of thyroid and pituitary hormones to the phenomena of metamorphosis in amphibians have been given elsewhere (Etkin, 1955). Etkin showed that there was always a build-up of the thyroxin concentration first. Recently,

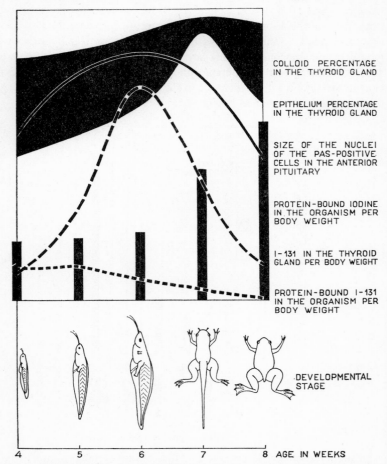

FIG. 9.7 Graphic diagram relating functional activity of thyroid gland to metamorphosis stages in *Xenopus laevis*. (From Saxen *et al.*, 1957, by kind permission of the authors.)

Tata (1965) observed enhanced RNA synthesis in the liver nuclei, 24 hr before morphological changes began. There are now possibilities of testing more closely the relationship between thyroxin concentration and biochemical changes, both by study of tissues such as the blood and the

DEVELOPMENTAL PROCESSES IN THE LARVA 141

retina where exact and rapid effects can be observed (see above) and in
isolated cultures of whole organs. It has to be borne in mind that culture
conditions do not reproduce the same situation as *in vivo*, however, for
they involve isolation from the pituitary and its thyrotropic effects. The
ultimobranchial bodies – glands that develop from the hindmost pair of
gill pouches – have been shown in *Xenopus* to have some endocrine
function during metamorphosis, too (Saxen and Toivönen, 1955). They
have follicles whose maximum size is attained at mid-metamorphosis,
but they do not accumulate iodine-131 (the radioactive isotope) as does
the thyroid. In detailed studies of the thyroid and pituitary in *Xenopus*,
these authors have observed that both glands show enhanced activity
before, as well as during, the metamorphosis period. A graphic summary
of their findings is given in Fig. 9.7 (from Saxen, Saxen, Toivönen and
Salimaki, 1957).

(iv) Special features of the regressing tail
Weber and his collaborators (see Weber and Niehus, 1961) have studied
in detail some of the enzyme activities in the regressing tail of *Xenopus
laevis* during metamorphosis. As might be expected, degradative
enzymes show large increases in activity: both cathepsin and acid
phosphatase activity increase sharply (Fig. 9.8). In the case of cathepsin,
there is an increased affinity of the enzyme for its substrate. Both Weber
(1962) and Shaffer (1963) have succeeded in isolating the tails in culture
and observing the effects of thyroxin and allied substances *in vivo*.
Weber found that the changes typical of metamorphosis took place in
the presence of 1 part/million of thyroxine. Shaffer produced the same
effects with tri-iodothyronine. When actinomycin D is added as well as
these agents, regression is inhibited, however (Tata, pers. comm. 1964).
So the regression evidently depends on synthesis of new, DNA-
dependent RNA as well as on breakdown processes. This somewhat un-
expected finding is being investigated further by Tata and his future
results should be very interesting.

Weber has gone on to show that the metamorphic changes induced *in
vitro* are accompanied by corresponding increases in hydrolytic enzyme
activities, just as in the intact animal. There is at least one enzyme – the
magnesium-activated ATPase considered characteristic of mitochondria
– whose activity *decreases* in the regressing tail. Salzmann and Weber

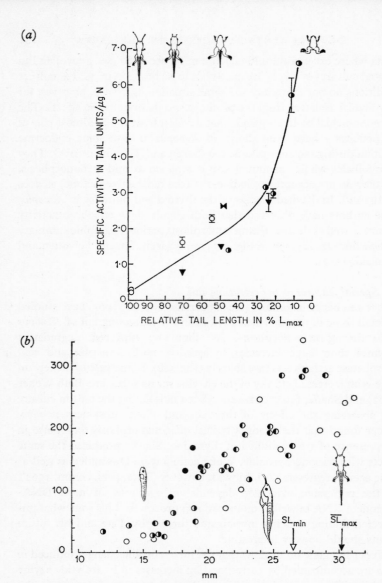

FIG. 9.8 Increases in (a) cathepsin activity and (b) acid phosphatase activity in regressing tail tissue of *Xenopus laevis* at metamorphosis. (From Weber, 1962; Weber and Niehus, 1961, by kind permission.)

(1963) have been able to locate acid phosphatase and cathepsin activity histochemically, finding it chiefly in the macrophages.

Weber (1964) went on to study the ultrastructural changes that accompany tail regression in *Xenopus*, concentrating particularly on the muscle cells, where there is a possibility of following the fate of the mitochondria in some detail.

(v) Concluding remarks on metamorphosis

Precise analysis of the biochemical effects of thyroxin has been undertaken in recent years, but we are still far from knowing what determines the highly different responses of different organs to this hormone. A striking example of the specificity of response is the difference between trunk and tail skin. When a thyroxin crystal is implanted into the fin, it induces, in the tail, spectacular degeneration of collagen (Gross, 1964). In the fin of the trunk, immediately adjacent to the implant, the same crystal will induce, in contrast, a build-up of new collagen fibres.* Moss and Ingram (1965) have also observed specific responses to thyroxin, in blood cells. Larval cells have their haemoglobin synthesis suppressed by the hormone, but the new line of cells that appears at metamorphosis has its haemoglobin synthesis stimulated by thyroxine.

The process of tail regression must involve a large-scale transfer of degradation products to other parts of the body, and we may assume that these are utilized for the formation of new tissues. Some of this material is lost by excretion, since the animals lose some weight during metamorphosis (Tata, pers. comm. 1964). But for the rest, the rate, scale, and sites of its transfer to the body have not yet been investigated. Most interesting possibilities may await discovery here. One wonders, for instance, whether any whole proteins can be transferred intact, for use in similar tissues (e.g. muscle myosin, skin collagen) that are growing in other regions during metamorphosis.

(c) Regeneration

Both the limbs and the tail of amphibians regenerate readily: in Urodeles, the regenerative ability is retained throughout life, but in

---

* Another interesting observation was that of Kollross (1942) who induced neuron proliferation, and maturation of the corneal reflex, in frog larvae by thyroxin crystals implanted into the hindbrain.

Anurans it is lost at metamorphosis. Earlier studies of biochemical events during regeneration have been reviewed by J. Needham (1942) and A. E. Needham (1952), so it is inappropriate to survey them again here in any detail. In brief summary, it may be said that at first, when tissue repair is taking place in the stump of a limb or tail after amputation, proteolytic (cathepsin) activity increases, reaching a maximum slightly earlier than the maximum concentration of free amino-acids.

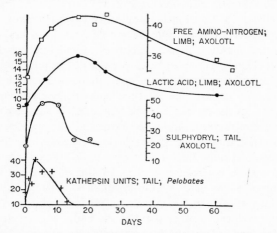

FIG. 9.9 Biochemical changes in the regenerating limb and tail of amphibians. (From Needham, 1942, *Biochemistry and Morphogenesis*.)

Graphs of dipeptidase activity and lactic acid production show similar trends (Fig. 9.9). Enzymes concerned with energy-releasing reactions *de*crease in activity, on the other hand, during this regression phase, then increase as the new tissue of the regenerate forms. We followed cathepsin activity separately in the tail stump and its regenerate, in *Xenopus laevis* (Deuchar, Weber, and Lehmann, 1957). Somewhat surprisingly, the specific catheptic activity in the regenerate was very high, despite the fact that it was growing and not regressing (Fig. 9.10). The point to be emphasized from this finding is that the *concentration* of enzyme (which is *not* measured, but only its *activity*) may possibly be constant in all these tissues, and simply its active properties change (there is, for instance, a change in the substrate affinity of *Xenopus* tail cathepsin (Weber, 1957) during metamorphosis). The concentration of free amino-acid, measured in the *Xenopus* tail regenerates and stumps, was found to increase slightly later than the increase in catheptic

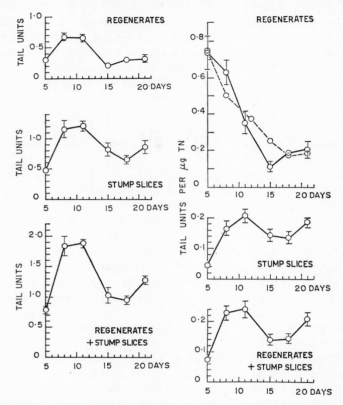

FIG. 9.10 Changes in cathepic activity in stump and regenerate of amputated tail tips of *Xenopus laevis*. (Deuchar, Weber, and Lehmann, 1957.) ('Tail units' = units of enzyme activity.)

activity. This is in accordance with expectation, since the amino-acids would be products of the enzymic breakdown of protein.

Apart from respiration studies (which indicate a low quotient during the regression phase but a greatly increased oxygen consumption later, in the repair phase), other aspects of the metabolism of regeneration in amphibian appendages have been neglected so far (cf. Needham, 1952). Once again the cogent problem as to how much original material is re-utilized in the newly-growing tissues (cf. p. 143) has been left un-tackled. So far, the tacit assumption has been that degradation products from the stump, such as amino-acids, are used as raw materials for synthesis of proteins in the regenerate. But no attempt has been made to trace these metabolites by radioactive labelling or, even more interest-ing, to trace whether any whole proteins are re-utilized for the same or other tissues of the regenerate. The work of Lehmann and his colleagues (see Lehmann, 1954) suggests that at least some amino-acids *as such* are the essential protein precursors, since treatments with amino-acid analogues inhibit regeneration, and this inhibition can be reversed by adding the normal amino-acid.

An extensive series of histochemical studies has been made on limb regenerates by Schmidt and his collaborators (see Schmidt and Weid-man, 1964). Most of the enzymes they studied (dehydrogenase, aldolase, acid and alkaline phosphatase, succinic, malic, and lactic dehydrogen-ases) were ubiquitously distributed, but with highest activities in the wound region, muscle, epidermis and subcutaneous glands. It has not so far been possible to assign any specialized function in regeneration to any of these enzymes, from this purely histochemical study.

Earlier, histological studies on regeneration have shown that stump cells 'dedifferentiate', losing all their special characteristics, in order to form the rounded blastema cells of the regenerate, which appear to have multiple potentialities. If these cells are indeed 'dedifferentiated', their nuclei should, like the nuclei of early embryonic cells, be capable of setting off normal development when transplanted into an enucleated egg (see Gurdon, 1963, 1964). This test has been tried by Burgess (not yet published) who finds, so far, that the blastema cells of regenerat-ing limbs of *Xenopus* can, in a few cases, set off development of the embryo up to a blastula-like stage. It is remarkable and interesting that they take it as far as this, but does not indicate that any dedifferentiation has occurred, by comparison with the nuclei of normal limb epidermis cells, which were also tested.

We know a little about the reappearance of proteins in the regenerat-ing limb. Laufer (1959) has identified actomyosin and myosin, by immunological methods, at the hand-formation stage in regenerating fore-limbs of the newt. Quinn (1962) made the interesting observation that tail regenerates lose antigenic materials as compared with normal tail tissue. This seems acceptable evidence of some degree of biochemical dedifferentiation in the cytoplasm.

Another problem still awaiting biochemical investigation is what causes the loss of regenerative ability in Anuran appendages (but not in Urodeles) from metamorphosis onwards. Rose (1944) claimed that limb regeneration could be induced in adult frogs by rubbing the limb stump with salt after amputation, so that no skin healing could take place. Though Rose's method was a little too naïve to be convincing, other evidence suggests that healing, and scar tissue, may be obstacles to re-generation. For instance one may mention here that the failure of the mammalian spinal cord to regenerate is believed to be due to scar tissue: treatment with pyrogenic agents that impede scar-formation may allow some transitory regeneration of fibres to take place. In amphibians, the cord of the trunk region is readily healed after tran-section, by fibre growth, but probably no new neurons are formed except at embryonic stages. In the tail, however, reserve cells from the ependymal layer remain capable of proliferating and reconstituting a complete spinal cord. The nature of the stimulus to regeneration is still unknown but may possibly be degeneration products from myelin. It is almost certainly a chemical stimulus. (For review of regeneration in the central nervous system of vertebrates, see Clemente, 1964.)

Singer (1952, 1959) concluded, from numerous experiments in-volving surgical deflection of the nerve-supply to regenerating limbs of salamanders, that the nerve-endings play some 'trophic' role in main-taining the regenerate. He points out that in adult Anurans and in higher vertebrates there are fewer nerve-endings peripherally, which may explain their inability to regenerate organs. He has not attempted to isolate any trophic factor biochemically, to date. It is impossible, in any case, to explain on his theory the ability of aneurogenic limbs (these were made to develop originally without a nerve supply) to regenerate also in the absence of nerves (Yntema, 1959). Steen and Thornton (1963) have shown that a skin graft from a normal limb on to the cap of an aneurogenic blastema will prevent its regeneration, but that if the graft is placed as a collar instead, leaving aneurogenic skin as the cap, regeneration will occur in the absence of nerves. Their results emphasize once more the importance of the tissue at the wound surface.

The phenomena of metamorphosis and regeneration in amphibians raise many extremely interesting problems that still remain unanswered. One feels tempted to conclude with a 'questionnaire' listing these, but it would not be fair to do this unless the morphological events had been described in considerable detail first. Such detail has not been possible in a book of this size and scope. But it is to be hoped that some biochemists will find this omission so provoking that they will go and read the relevant descriptions and look for new research projects in this field.

CHAPTER TEN

General Survey and Conclusions

Throughout this book, each morphological stage has been dealt with separately so far. This was in order to emphasize the special problems of development that have interested embryologists in the past, and are amenable to biochemical investigation. It is now proposed, however, to conclude by reviewing the events of embryonic development as a whole and to follow the course of some biochemical changes over the whole period. This is essentially the biochemist's method of treating the subject and the traditional embryologist may strongly object to it. With the concept of 'molecular embryology' in mind, however, he ought now to be prepared to derive as much satisfaction from a study of the changes in shape, size, and structure of molecules in embryonic cells as he used to from his study of the visible changes in the whole embryo. The fact that he probably does not enjoy this prospect yet, is due to the highly abstract thinking that is still necessary. We cannot yet 'see' molecules changing before our very eyes, whereas we can see blastomeres dividing or, with suitable time-lapse filming, watch the movements and differentiation of gastrula and neurula tissues. It requires considerable effort and the pulling together of many different kinds of evidence to synthesize a mental picture of the development of molecules and their reactions in the embryo. This is what, in this chapter, we shall attempt to do. It must be realized at the outset that the picture will be very bare and diagrammatic, for accurate drawings cannot be made except from visual observation – an impossibility with most of the information that we are dealing with here.

One of the kinds of diagram with which any account of events over the period of embryonic development is bound to be peppered is the 'time curve'. This graphic way of depicting apparently continuous quantitative change taking place during the hours, days, weeks, or months of an animal's development, is liable to certain fallacies, however, which should be made clear at the outset. There is, first, the fallacy of *joining up* the points on the graph, when the time spanned on the horizontal axis is enormously greater than that for most biochemical reactions. All too often, owing to sparsity of data from the minute quantities of material that can laboriously be collected, the points lie too far apart for a linear join justifiably to be made between them unless the time scale is reduced out of all reasonable proportion. Who is to say that there are not extreme and important fluctuations in the intervening periods between any two points? It is better practice first to plot the points as a 'scatter diagram' and establish whether there is any statistical trend with time. Unfortunately, many authors fail to do this.

The other problem that arises in connexion with time curves of events in embryonic development is whether the time scale used should really be linear. When the embryo is changing in a peculiar series of highly different steps with unequal time intervals between them, should not the shape of the curve be related to these steps rather than to constant time units? This is the morphologist's argument and one of his main objections to the biochemist's brash 'overall' view which so often takes too little account of morphological changes. Two Russian authors, Dettlaff and Dettlaff (1961) have in fact suggested using a scale related to morphological changes and independent of time. It is doubtful if this idea will be widely accepted, however. For a complete and balanced picture, the only expedient is to use more than one method of plotting one's data. This is, in effect, the course taken in this book. We have looked, first, at the single points on the various curves in their 'vertical' relationship to the individual morphological stages and are now about to plot the data in the other way, along time scales of minutes, hours, or days. We may now hope to see whether there are continuous biochemical changes which might appear as reasonable causes of some of the morphological changes of embryonic development.

(a) Time curves for respiration during embryonic development
Measurements of the oxygen consumption by embryos are among some of the earliest for which suitable micro-methods were devised and some of these data that have been plotted as time curves are, therefore, very old. They show, in general, a steep increase at least up to hatching but

with variations in different species of amphibians. One common feature which has been commented on particularly by Løvtrup (1959) and Tuft (1953) is the flattening of such time curves – indicating a lower rate of increase in oxygen consumption – at neurulation (cf. Fig. 10.1 – from Boell (1955)). Løvtrup goes so far as to say that there is a more or less constant oxygen uptake over this period and also during a brief period in larval development (Fig. 10.2 a). These results have to be explained

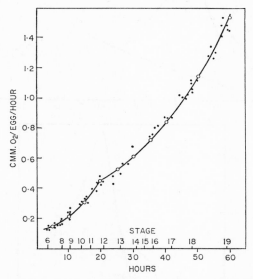

FIG. 10.1 Time curve of oxygen consumption throughout early development in *Rana pipiens*. (From Boell, 1955.)

on the bases, both of the total energy consumption of the embryo and of the sources of energy used, since the respiratory quotient depends on these. Løvtrup attributes the first flattening of the curve to the switch-over from carbohydrate to fat as a source of energy (Fig. 10.2 b), assuming that the fat is not at first used at a maximal rate, though the availability of carbohydrates has already decreased. At later phases, both fat and carbohydrate sources become increasingly available and eventually, when feeding starts, protein predominates as a source of

L

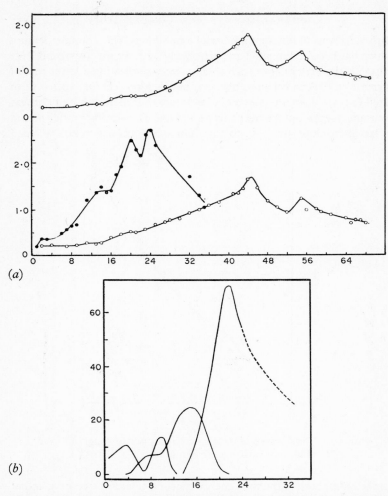

FIG. 10.2 (a) Oxygen consumption throughout embryonic and larval development. Respiratory curves with two horizontal phases and two maxima. Filled circles: 18° C. Open circles: 10° C. Ordinate: μl. O₂/hr per embryo. Abscissa: days. (b) Consumption of energy sources during embryonic development. Changes in the rate of consumption of energy sources. First curve: carbohydrate; second curve: fat; third curve: protein. Ordinate: μg/24 hr/embryo. Abscissa: days. (From Løvtrup, 1959, by kind permission of the author.)

energy. Løvtrup (loc. cit.) is at pains to point out that the respiratory curve should not be thought of either as two exponential growth curves with a break between them, or as an expression only of the rate of cell division. He and Werdinius (1957) prefer to think of *three* phases of increase, the first associated with gastrulation, the second with larval ectoderm development, and the third with the final differentiation of the endoderm.

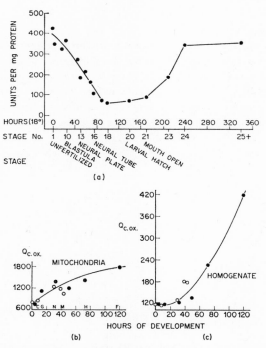

FIG. 10.3 (*a*) Data of Lang and Grant (1961) on *Rana pipiens*; (*b*) and (*c*) Data of Boell and Weber (1955) on *Xenopus laevis*: Graphs showing the cytochrome oxidase activity of homogenates and mitochondria of *Xenopus laevis* embryos at various stages of development. The ordinate represents *specific activity of cytochrome oxidase* as m μl oxygen per μg protein nitrogen per hour. The abscissa denotes *developmental stage* in hours from time of fertilization. Values at zero hours were derived from time of fertilization. Values at zero hours were derived from ovarian eggs.

(b) Time curves of respiratory enzyme activities

The availability of energy sources is controlled by activities of enzymes that oxidize them as well as by those that break down larger molecules. Many of the enzymes directly concerned with respiratory metabolism have been followed through amphibian development and we shall mention here only the more recent work on these. The reader is referred to Brachet's (1960) or Needham's (1942) books for a more extensive review and for details of the earlier work.

Cytochrome oxidase

According to Boell and Weber (1955) there is an exponential increase of cytochrome oxidase activity during development of *Xenopus* from cleavage to feeding larval stages (*if the points on their graph are directly joined*). Sixty per cent of this enzyme activity is in the mitochondrial fraction of homogenates. Although the mitochondria increase in number over the same period, it is clear that their individual enzyme

Specific Activity[a] of Enzymes in Mitochondria from Embryonic and Larval Tissues of Xenopus (Weber and Boell, 1962).

Mitochondria from	CYTO-CHROME OXIDASE Q	R	ATPASE Q	R	ACID PHOS-PHATASE Q	R	CATHEPSIN Q	R
Tailbud embryo	1,038	1·0	4·55	1·0	0·70	1·0	7·18	1·0
Dorsal half 'mesoderm'	2,493	2·4	8·86	1·9	2·38	3·4	10·56	1·5
Ventral half 'endoderm'	768	0·7	5·52	1·2	0·76	1·1	5·22	0·7
Tail muscle	2,030	2·0	18·5	4·1	0·72	1·0	7·07	1·0
Liver	649	0·6	32·3	7·1	10·5	15·0	35·8	5·0

[a] Q = specific activity; R = ratio of activity compared with tailbud embryo. Data in 'activity units'.

FIG. 10.4 Cytochrome oxidase and other enzyme activities in mitochondria from different tissues of *Xenopus laevis*.

activity must also increase to account for the very steep rise in total activity. In contrast, Lang and Grant (1961) obtain decreasing activities in *Rana pipiens* (Fig. 10.3). More recently Weber and Boell (1962) have compared the cytochrome oxidase activities of different larval and embryonic tissues and found that they follow different patterns during development. Liver mitochondria, which have relatively few cristae visible under the electron microscope, have lower activities than muscle mitochondria whose cristae are more numerous (Fig. 10.4). There seems a promise here that the enzyme activities may eventually be explained in terms of structural changes, either of the enzyme molecules themselves or of the sites at which they aggregate in the mitochondrion.

Citric acid cycle enzymes
Little is known of their activity in early stages, although succin-oxidase has been shown to be present by stage 20 in the salamander

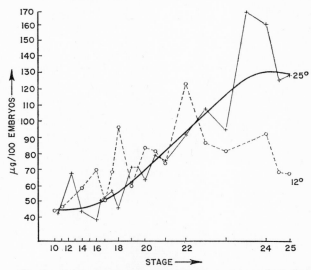

FIG. 10.5 Citric acid content of *Rana esculenta* embryos during development. (From Ten Cate, 1959, with kind permission of the author.)

Ambystoma punctatum (Boell, 1948). Citric acid itself is synthesized in *Rana esculenta* embryos in concentrations that apparently fluctuate, according to the curve published by Ten Cate (1959) (Fig. 10.5). Wallace (1961) also obtained measures of isocitric dehydrogenase activity,

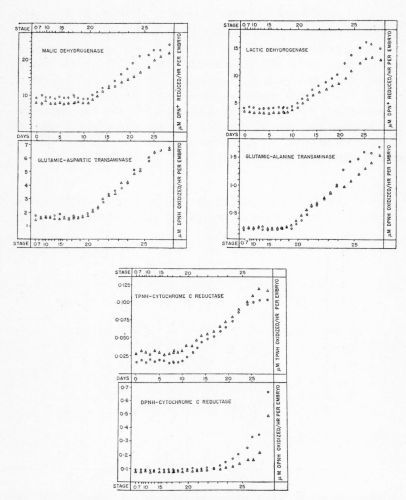

FIG. 10.6 Enzyme activities during development in *Rana*. (From Wallace, 1961, with author's permission.) (See text for further particulars.)

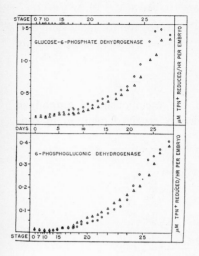

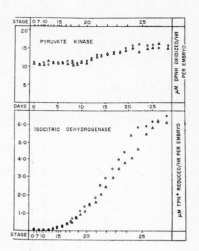

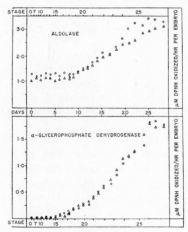

FIG. 10.6 (*contd.*)

which did not increase before stage 15 in *Rana*, and for malic dehydrogenase activity which showed high levels at earlier stages. His data are given in Fig. 10.6.

Oxygen consumption in hybrids

Chen's extensive studies (1953) on the metabolism of amphibian hybrids during development have already received mention in con-

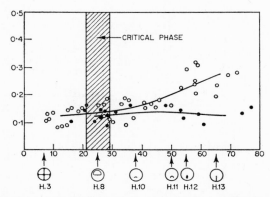

FIG. 10.7 Oxygen consumption in *Triturus palmatus* and *Salamandra atra* hybrids (black circles) compared with normal *T. palmatus* embryos (white circles). (From Chen (1953), with permission.) Diagrams below show stages.

nexion with the role of nuclear factors in early embryos. His graphs (Fig. 10.7) show that the oxygen consumption in *Triturus palmatus* × *Salamandra atra* hybrids, like many other metabolic processes, fails to increase after gastrulation. In fact, the hybrids fail to gastrulate and remain as early gastrulae until they die.

Utilization of glycogen

Cohen (1954) followed the course of anaerobic glycolysis during development of *Rana pipiens*, up to the neurula stage. His somewhat sparse data suggest a linear increase of lactate production with time. Comparing glycogen disappearance with lactate production, he concludes that some of the glycogen must be utilized for other purposes such as synthesis.

Aldolase activity and lactic dehydrogenase activity have also been followed, in *Rana pipiens*, by Wallace (1961) who found essentially constant activities till after hatching when there was a rise (Fig. 10.6).

(c) Time curves of other enzyme activities during embryonic development

Løvtrup (1955, 1960) has reviewed the course of enzyme activities in amphibian development. He considers that the enzymes fall into two

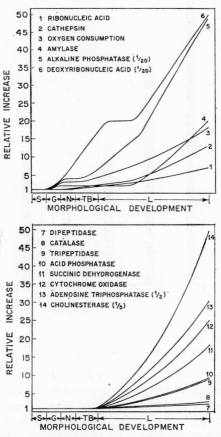

FIG. 10.8 Time curves of enzyme activities during embryonic development. (From Løvtrup, 1955.)

groups: those that are constant in activity till after hatching, and those that show their first increase in activity during gastrulation. Løvtrup's graphical representations are given in Fig. 10.8. Our own data on cathepsin activity do not, however, agree with the course of the curve

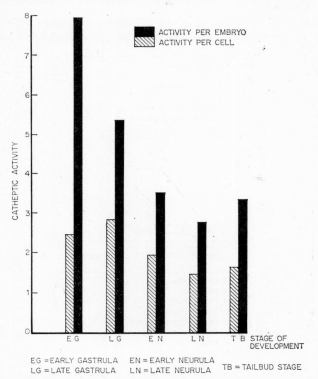

FIG. 10.9 Histogram to illustrate changes in cathepsin activity during embryonic development in *Xenopus laevis*. (Deuchar, 1958 *b*.)

he gives (cf. Fig. 10.9). The possibility has to be entertained that those enzymes whose activity has not been *observed* to change before hatching may not have been assayed by sufficiently sensitive methods. Looking back now at the earlier work on enzyme activities it must be realized that much of it was pioneering and that sufficient attention may not have been paid to establishing the characteristics of the reaction such as its Michaelis constant and optimal assay conditions. It may be noted that Wallace (loc. cit.), using newer methods, found increases in several enzyme activities at neurulation and not at gastrulation. Løvtrup's distinction between the two types of enzyme activity time curve was in any case a matter only of convenience for graphical representation. It clearly bears no relation to the function of the enzymes, for some proteolytic enzymes and some parameters connected with respiration, as well as a phosphatase, appear in each group. At all events, it is clear from the remarks made above that the horizontal regions of the curves in Fig. 10.8 express chiefly our ignorance or lack of adequate assay methods for these early stages.

A point that should be stressed is that increases of enzyme *activity* do not necessarily mean a synthesis of enzyme: they may reflect a change in its physiological state – i.e. it may have been partially inactivated before – or a change in its substrate affinity (shown by its Michaelis constant). So far, no systematic measurements of quantities of purified enzyme from embryonic tissues have been achieved. It would, indeed, be difficult to detect such small protein increases by ordinary bio-chemical methods involving nitrogen determination. The total nitrogen in amphibian embryos remains remarkably constant up to hatching (Gregg and Ballentine, 1946; Wills, 1936).

(d) Time curves for DNA concentration
The probability that cytoplasmic DNA furnishes source material for synthesis of nuclear DNA has already been discussed (Chapter Four, p. 58). This makes sense of the curves which show, although some DNA increase in early stages, not nearly enough to account for doubling at each cleavage. The form of the curves reproduced by various authors show considerable variations, however, which Bristow and Deuchar (1964) have suggested may be eliminable by more careful repetition and by attention, in some cases, to the standard deviations of the data. Some interesting but little-known results of Vilmikova and Nedvidek (1962) are shown in Fig. 10.10 for comparison with ours and with those of Chen (1960). It is doubtful whether time curves of normal DNA increase have much value except as a basis of reference in connexion with other quantitative studies. What is of more significance is that the total DNA per cell reaches the adult figure by the tailbud stage (see

Species	BRACHET (1941)		STEINERT (1951)			CHEN (1960)			BRISTOW AND DEUCHAR (1964)
	Rana fusca	*Amby-stoma mexi-canum*	*Amby-stoma mexi-canum*	*Rana fusca*	*Rana esculenta*	*Triturus alpestris*	*Triturus palmatus*	*Triturus cristatus*	*Xenopus laevis*
Fertilized egg	2·75	4·75	11	13·00	—	2·8	2·0	3·5	4·4
Morula	—	—	11·5	14·10	4·1	2·8	2·0	3·5	4·7
Blastula	—	—	12	15·40	—	2·8	2·0	3·5	4·9
Early gastrula	3·1	5·1	13	15·50	4·3	2·8	2·1	3·5	5·2
Late gastrula	—	—	14	—	—	2·9	2·4	3·6	5·5
Neurula	—	7·25	17	—	—	3·3	2·8	3·8	5·7
Tailbud	—	—	21	—	5·7	3·7	3·2	4·5	5·9
Tadpole	4·6	7·25	—	—	—	—	—	—	7·3

(*RNA concentrations: µg. per embryo*)

FIG. 10.10 Comparison of various authors' data on DNA concentrations during embryonic development in amphibians. (For references, see text.)

Fig. 10.11), indicating that the cytoplasmic DNA is fully utilized by then. Further, it is clear from the blockage of DNA synthesis in hybrids (Chen and Zeller, 1961) that the cytoplasmic DNA in these makes an

| Stage | No. of cells | Xenopus laevis | |
		RNA/cell (μg)	DNA/cell (μg)
Uncleaved	1	4·4	0·52
Morula	50	$9·4 \times 10^{-2}$	$0·15 \times 10^{-1}$
Blastula	2,500	$2·0 \times 10^{-3}$	$0·32 \times 10^{-3}$
Early gastrula	40,000	$1·3 \times 10^{-4}$	$0·26 \times 10^{-4}$
Early neurula	100,000	$5·5 \times 10^{-5}$	$0·13 \times 10^{-4}$
Late neurula	180,000	$3·2 \times 10^{-5}$	$0·88 \times 10^{-5}$
Initial tailbud	215,000	$2·7 \times 10^{-5}$	$0·84 \times 10^{-5}$
Hatching	250,000	$2·5 \times 10^{-5}$	$0·84 \times 10^{-5}$

| Stage | Rana pipiens (Sze, 1953) | |
	No. of cells	DNA/cell (μg)
Uncleaved	1	0·96
Morula	—	—
Blastula	3,100	$0·42 \times 10^{-3}$
Early gastrula	3,200	$0·42 \times 10^{-4}$
Early neurula	98,000	$0·24 \times 10^{-4}$
Late neurula	172,000	$0·17 \times 10^{-4}$
Initial tailbud	—	—
Hatching	440,000	$0·14 \times 10^{-4}$

FIG. 10.11 Concentrations of RNA and DNA per cell on *Xenopus laevis* embryos (Bristow and Deuchar, 1964), compared with the DNA per cell in *Rana pipiens* embryos (Sze, 1953).

unfavourable partnership with foreign nuclear DNA. It must, therefore, have some specific structure although it is not embodied in chromosomes.

The chromosomes of amphibian embryos need a great deal of further study: unfortunately, they are much smaller and more difficult to observe than the 'lampbrush' chromosomes (Callan, 1964) of oocyte stages. It would be most interesting to see if any characteristic 'puffs' such as those described in insects (Beerman, 1956) appear in chromosomes of the various tissues as they differentiate. If so, these might indicate the synthesis of special 'messenger' RNA. We also need to know more about the structure of the basic proteins (histones) of the

chromosome. Moore (1963) has shown that histones are being synthesized from very early (pre-gastrula) stages of development onwards, in
Rana. Histones are thought to be capable of acting as differential
repressors of gene activity. Their possible role in embryogenesis has
been re-emphasized by Brachet (1964), and Barth and Barth (1964)
have pointed out that it is only necessary to postulate one histone
controlling each sequence of reactions, in sequential inductions such as
they have demonstrated (see p. 111).

(e) Time curves for RNA concentration

There is much the same disagreement between time curves for RNA
concentration in the embryo as with the curves for DNA, and these may
also almost certainly be attributed to the inadequacy and wide statistical
variance of many authors' data. One should comment, perhaps, in self-
defence, that measurements of this kind are extremely difficult to reproduce successfully with this material. Different batches of eggs, even
from the same mating on different occasions, vary considerably in their
quantitative biochemical properties. The only satisfactory way to set
up an experiment is to aim to collect all the material from one batch
of eggs – but this may result in only a few samples of each embryonic
stage. At least, the data agree in showing an increase of RNA, but the
time of onset of this increase is probably earlier (Bristow and Deuchar)
than many authors have supposed. Fig. 10.12 sets out these comparisons.

In their important recent investigation, Brown and Littna (1964 *a*)
studied in a sucrose density gradient the forms of RNA synthesized at
different stages of development in *Xenopus laevis*. They found a significant synthesis of ribosomal RNA at the onset of gastrulation, at the
time when the nucleoli first appear. This ribosomal RNA synthesis
increases at later stages, and the proportions of other components
(characterized in Fig. 10.13) alter slightly too. The logical extension of
their work, which is now being undertaken (Deuchar and Evans, unpublished), is to see whether any different forms of RNA may be de-
tected in the various tissues of the early embryo, coincident with
moments of enhanced synthesis of a particular protein. Organs such as
endocrine glands, which undergo 'bursts' of synthesis of a hormone at
certain moments like metamorphosis, might be suitable for such studies
too. Brown's former colleague, Caston (1962), has noted the time of first

AUTHOR		CHEN		GRANT	VILMIKOVA AND NEDVIDEK		BRISTOW AND DEUCHAR
Species	Triturus alpestris	Triturus palmatus	Triturus cristatus	Rana pipiens	Rana temporaria	Xenopus laevis	Xenopus laevis
Fertilized egg	2·5	1·5	1·2	0·022	—	—	0·52
Morula	2·5	1·5	1·2	0·025	—	—	0·75
Blastula	2·5	1·6	1·3	0·102	1·80	0·55	0·79
Early gastrula	2·5	1·8	1·8	0·563	1·89	0·88	1·0
Late gastrula	4·5	4·3	2·8	1·11	—	1·30	1·3
Neurula	6·7	6·4	4·6	1·87	3·15	—	1·6
Tailbud	8·8	—	—	3·99	—	—	1·8

FIG. 10.12 Concentrations of total RNA per embryo, during development in amphibians – data of several authors compared. (For references, see text.)

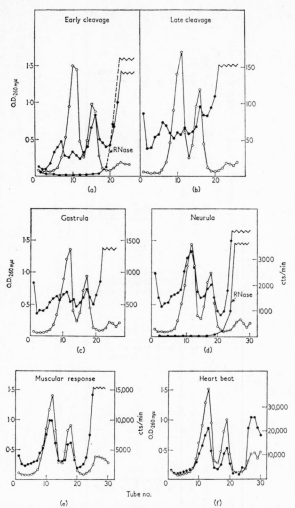

FIG. 10.13 Density-gradient analyses of RNA from *Xenopus laevis* embryos at various stages of development. Each density gradient centrifugation was performed on RNA isolated from 150 embryos. The stages (Nieuwkoop and Faber, 1956), and hours after fertilization of each group of embryos are: (*a*) early cleavage (2–7), 1·5–3 hr; (*b*) late cleavage (8–9), 5–6 hr; (*c*) gastrula (10–11), 28 hr; (*d*) neurula (13–14), 34 hr; (*e*) muscular response (25–26), 54 hr; (*f*) heart beat (33–34), 74 hr. –○–, O. D; –●–, radioactivity. (From Brown and Littna, 1954, by kind permission.)

appearance of noradrenaline in *Rana pipiens* (stages 15–16) but has not made quantitative estimations of this hormone throughout development. New facts about the significance of nucleolar RNA are now emerging from the work of Brown and Gurdon (loc. cit., p. 47) on anucleolate mutants of *Xenopus laevis*. Wallace (1962) has observed intranuclear 'blobs' like aberrant nucleoli in these mutants. He confirms that the larvae are deficient in both RNA and DNA by the time of hatching.

(f) Patterns of protein synthesis throughout development

(i) *An enzyme of special function: cholinesterase*
It was pointed out in Chapter Seven that the presence of cholinesterase activity could be considered as one of the special biochemical character-istics of neural tissue and that if it appeared early enough it might be the best chemical criterion for neural induction having taken place. Although we still do not know if this enzyme is present as early as the neurula stage, or whether it is inducible by any of the usual neural inducing agents, we do know more about its overall synthesis during later embryonic development, thanks to the work of Boell and Shen and their colleagues (1950, 1955). Their main achievement was to show that the increase in cholinesterase activity synchronizes with the appearance of motility and to demonstrate histochemically that it appears in synapse layers of the brain, retina, and spinal cord as soon as these become distinct. It is interesting that Ten Cate, Kooij, and Zuidweg (1951) showed that the time of synthesis of cholinesterase remained dependent strictly on the stage of development reached and on the degree of motility, at lowered temperatures. This is in contrast to Ten Cate's finding (see Woerdeman, 1939) that induction of the lens proceeded independently of the morphological stage of development, at low temperature.

(ii) *Enzymes of wide distribution*
Weber and Boell (1962, loc. cit. above) studied ATPase, acid phos-phatase, and cathepsin activities parallel with their studies of cytochrome oxidase activity in whole homogenates and isolated mitochondria of *Xenopus* embryonic tissues. They were interested in following the course of events during development, but unfortunately their data refer only

M

to two distinct stages. The main finding was a distinction in the enzymes' properties in the different organs. The data are given in Fig. 10.4.

One of the enzymes included in Løvtrup's group that increase at

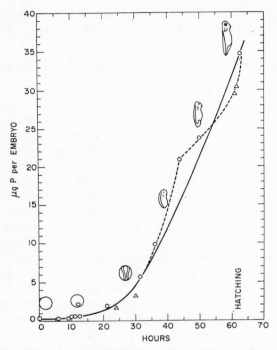

FIG. 10.14 Alkaline phosphatase activity throughout development in *Xenopus laevis*. (From Krugelis, 1950.)

gastrulation is alkaline phosphatase. Its most dramatic increase is at stage 21. Krugelis (1950) paid particular attention to the course of alkaline phosphatase activity in the development of *Ambystoma punctatum* and *Xenopus laevis* (Fig. 10.14). She found highest activity in dorsal regions at all the stages tried.

Kurata (1962) tried to see evidence of biochemical 'recapitulation' in the appearance of what he considered were 'primitive' anaerobic

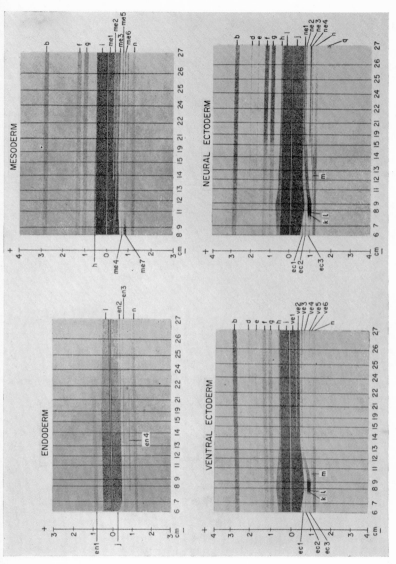

FIG. 10.15 Electrophoretograms of proteins extracted from different tissues of *Pleurodeles* embryos. (From Denis, 1961.) Letters = different protein bands. Figures on abscissa = stages of development.

enzymes – hydrogenase, nitrate reductase, and aspartase – at early embryonic stages in the frog. These have sharp peaks of activity at gastrula, neurula, and tailbud stages, respectively. However, his argument for 'recapitulation' is unconvincing and has not been supported by any evidence of the enzymes' sequence of appearance in other vertebrate embryos.

One of the most careful recent studies of enzyme activities in amphibian development is that of Wallace (loc. cit. above, 1961), who worked out fully the assay conditions for twelve key enzymes of carbohydrate/protein metabolism using pyridine nucleotide fluorimetry. Many of these enzymes showed increases first at the neurula stage: others not till hatching (Fig. 10.6).

Before leaving the subject of enzyme development, a reminder may be added that the appearance of these enzymes, as well as the increases in their activity, must be governed by quite complex control processes. Attempts to demonstrate enzyme induction in amphibian embryos by small metabolites (substrates) have not so far met with much success: Spiegel and Frankel (1961) have failed to induce tryptophan peroxidase activity in *Rana pipiens* at any stage prior to metamorphosis, although Stearns and Kostellow (1958) claimed that this was possible at the gastrula stage. Despite the lack of evidence in amphibians, there are more positive examples in chick embryos (cf. review by Wilt, 1964) and there is every reason to suppose that enzyme induction occurs during embryonic development just as it does in adult tissues and in bacteria (Pollock, 1959). For this reason, the concentrations of small metabolites such as free amino-acids (see later, p. 178) may have significance in controlling embryonic differentiation at certain crucial moments.

(iii) Tissue-specific antigens

Mention has already been made of the work of Inoue (1961 *a* and *b*) and of Denis (1961) in which the appearance of a number of different antigens was followed in whole embryos. Some of Denis's and Inoue's results are depicted in Figs. 10.15 and 10.16. They show quite clearly that there are tissue-specific differences and are a valuable extension of Clayton's study (1953) of the distribution of antigens in different regions of gastrulae and neurulae, which was mentioned previously

Serological Active Groups in S-fractions of Early Embryonic Stages against
Anti-S-fraction Sera (Inoue, 1961)

Antigen × antibody	—SH	—S—S—	Phenol	Amino	Imidazol
LOS × anti-LOS	+	+	+		
LOS × anti-MS	2+	+			
LOS × anti-G$_1$S					
LOS × anti-G$_2$S					
LOS × anti-NS					
LOS × anti-TBS					
MS × anti-LOS	2+	+			
MS × anti-MS	3+	3+			+
MS × anti-G$_1$S	2+	2+			+
MS × anti-G$_2$S	+	2+			+
MS × anti-NS	2+	2+		+	+
MS × anti-TBS		2+		+	+
BS × anti-LOS	2+				
BS × anti-MS	3+				+
BS × anti-G$_1$S	2+	+	2+	+	+
BS × anti-G$_2$S	2+	+	+	+	+
BS × anti-NS	2+	+	+	2+	+
BS × anti-TBS				+	+
G$_1$S × anti-LOS	+				
G$_1$S × anti-MS	2+	+			+
G$_1$S × anti-G$_1$S	2+	3+	3+	+	2+
G$_1$S × anti-G$_2$S	2+	3+	3+	2+	2+
G$_1$S × anti-NS	+	2+	2+	2+	2+
G$_1$S × anti-TBS		+	+	2+	+
G$_2$S × anti-LOS					
G$_2$S × anti-MS	2+	+			+
G$_2$S × anti-G$_1$S	+	3+	3+	+	2+
G$_2$S × anti-G$_2$S	+	3+	3+	2+	2+
G$_2$S × anti-NS	+	+	3+	2+	2+
G$_2$S × anti-TBS		+	+	2+	+
NS × anti-LOS					
NS × anti-MS		+			+
NS × anti-G$_1$S		2+	+	+	+
NS × anti-G$_2$S	+	2+	3+	3+	2+
NS × anti-NS	+	+	2+	3+	2+
NS × anti-TBS		+		3+	+
TBS × anti-LOS					
TBS × anti-MS					+
TBS × anti-G$_1$S				+	+
TBS × anti-G$_2$S	+	+		3+	2+
TBS × anti-NS	+	+		3+	2+
TBS × anti-TBS	+			3+	+

3+, 2+, and + indicate relative degree of activity in antigen–antibody reactions.

FIG. 10.16 Tabulation of different serologically active groups present
in proteins at different stages of development. (From Inoue, 1961.)
LO = large oocyte; M = morula; B = blastula; G$_1$ = early gastrula;
G$_2$ = late gastrula; N = neurula; TB = tailbud stage.

(p. 72). Special attention should also be drawn again to Romanovsky's less widely-known work (1964), since he noted several transient, stage-specific antigens in early embryos of *Rana esculenta* that were *lost* later in development: an interesting further example (cf. p. 93) of the fact that differentiation sometimes involves losses, as well as gains, of special

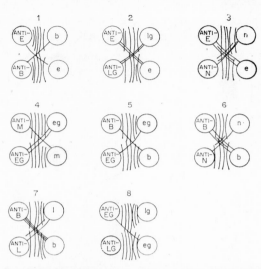

FIG. 10.17 Precipitation lines in reactions of antigens from different developmental stages. Precipitation lines specific for one or both systems transect the spectrum of lines common to both compared systems diagonally. (From Romanovsky, 1964.)

proteins. Romanovsky concludes that the egg, the morula and blastula, the early and late gastrula, and the neurula and tailbud stage have quite different group antigenicities – four in all (Fig. 10.17).

As is well known, individuals are normally non-reactive to their own antigens and to any antigens to which they have been made 'tolerant' by being presented with them during embryonic life before the immune mechanism has developed (Billingham, Brent, and Medawar, 1956). Hildemann (1962) has shown that amphibians should be particularly convenient for experiments on the induction of tolerance, since larvae of quite advanced age (40 days, in the bullfrog) can successfully be made

M 2

tolerant to homografts. After this age, the immune mechanism develops and grafts are rejected.

(g) Yolk utilization and protein turnover during development

It is fair to say that the main biochemical event of embryonic development in amphibians is the conversion of yolk into tissue proteins. This is a gradual process starting at different times in different parts of the embryo and extending into larval life as well. There are two kinds of

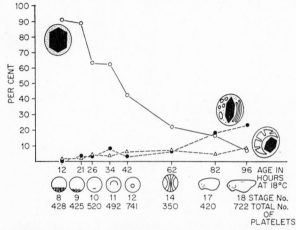

FIG. 10.18 Graphic representation of the course of yolk breakdown during amphibian development. (From Karasaki, 1963.)

evidence from which the rate and location of yolk breakdown can be judged: microscopical and biochemical. We shall deal mostly with the latter but it will be helpful to preface the account by a reference to at least one of the electron microscope observations of yolk breakdown that are becoming steadily more numerous. Karasaki's work (1963 a and b) has already been mentioned: his summary charts of the changes from cleavage to hatching stage in *Rana pipiens* are given here (Fig. 10.18). Symbolic of the controversy as to whether or not the breakdown is mediated by mitochondria is his extremely ambiguous drawing of a 'mitochondrion' with yolk platelet inside it, elsewhere. We await with impatience the application of radioactive tracer methods to this kind of electron microscopic study, so that the fate of labelled yolk materials may be followed with certainty instead of by guesswork from necessarily incomplete series of static pictures. The utilization of yolk in the notochord has been followed in some detail by Jurand and Selman (1964) from electron microscope pictures. Selman and Pawsey (1965) have also made a comparative survey of the rates of yolk platelet breakdown in embryonic tissues. The chorda-mesoderm is, in fact, one of the earliest regions to lose all its yolk.

Flickinger (1960) noted from biochemical estimations of protein and ribonucleoprotein of *Rana* that yolk is broken down extensively in the chorda-mesoderm during gastrulation, but not until neurulation in the ectoderm. This breakdown was judged from increased solubilization of the yolk constituents. The most specific of the enzymes concerned in solubilization of yolk phosphoproteins is phosphoprotein phosphatase, which Flickinger believes to be present in pigment (cf. p. 42). The course of activity of this enzyme has not been followed through development: Flickinger attempted to plot *graphically* the three values he obtained for its activity at oocyte, yolk plug, and hatching stages, however! His finding of a higher activity at hatching than at the earlier stages is credible, but there may be a maximimum (or minimum) at some other stage.

The main class of enzymes also involved in yolk breakdown are the cathepsins. During embryonic development in *Xenopus*, there appears to be a particular increase of catheptic activity during gastrulation and at the early neurula stage. There is then apparently a decrease in activity during neurulation, and an increase again at the tailbud stage (Deuchar, 1958 b). Other authors such as Urbani (1955) and Vecchioli (1956) have failed to observe any significant changes in catheptic activity in early embryos of *Bufo*, however, possibly owing to insensitivity of their methods.

At the 'output end' of protein breakdown, increases in peptides and in the free amino-acid 'pool' are observed. Kutsky et al. (1953), Chen (1956), and I (1956) measured concentrations of free amino-acids during development in three different amphibian species. Our results, some of which are summarized graphically in Fig. 10.19, show a considerable measure of agreement. The chief point to notice is that 'essential' amino-acids that cannot be synthesized in mammals and are not involved in carbohydrate metabolism, are the ones that do not increase in concentration until later in development when there has been considerable yolk breakdown. In *Xenopus* there is, as a whole, a slight fall in the concentration of total free amino-acid during embryonic development. It may be assumed that normally a balance is maintained between free and protein-bound amino-acid concentrations: for instance, it has

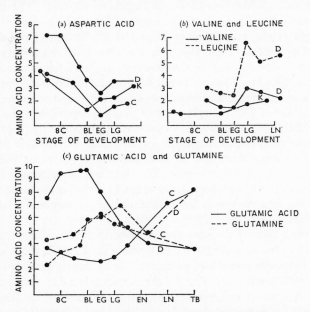

FIG. 10.19 Concentrations of free amino-acids during amphibian development. K = from Kutsky *et al.* (1953) on *Rana*; C = data of Chen (1956) on *Triturus*; D = Deuchar (1956) on *Xenopus*.

been found that increasing the 'pool' concentrations of free amino-acids experimentally inhibits yolk-breakdown in myoblast cells in tissue culture (Flickinger, 1949).

There are, then, several indications that the supply of raw materials for the synthesis of gradually diversifying proteins during embryonic development is normally very precisely regulated. As a result, the different tissues come to differ biochemically from each other in ways that are specific, not so much to the species of animal as to the kind of tissue. Thus there are biochemical resemblances between similar tissues of various vertebrate animals. Roberts *et al.* (1949, 1957) were the first to suggest that distinctive free amino-acid patterns could be recognized in different adult tissues. For this reason, the few similarities in free amino-acid pattern to those of adult tissues, that could be recognized in *Xenopus* embryos (Deuchar, loc. cit., 1956), were of some interest (see p. 74). Though it would be too naïve to expect that a recognizably distinct free amino-acid pattern would precede the synthesis of each special tissue protein, the characteristic free amino-acid patterns that *are* recognizable must be considered as in some way indicators of the kind of protein synthesis (and breakdown) going on in each tissue. It is a question of finding and choosing the right tissue for useful discoveries. The best is some tissue whose protein complement is predominantly of one kind. Unfortunately, all too few examples of such tissues are known. Erythrocytes, with their very high percentage of haemoglobin, are one; connective tissue, with its high collagen content recognized by the hydroxyproline that is unique to this protein, is another. It has not yet been observed whether either of these tissues has a distinctive free amino-acid complement, but some of their other biochemical characteristics are well known in adults and would be worth looking for in embryos, too.

(h) Conclusion: the biochemical basis of differentiation

It may seem an unwarranted digression to bring in here some mention of the characteristics of cancerous (tumour) cells. But in the work that has just been referred to above, Roberts and Frankel (1949) pointed out that free amino-acid patterns in tumours differed considerably from those of the corresponding normal tissues. One particular feature of tumours is their deficiency of free glutamine and that, remarkably, the glutamine concentration increases whenever they regress under various treatments. It has been suggested that one of the adverse effects of tumour cells on the tissues round them is to take up glutamine from the normal tissues to supplement their own deficiency, since they seem incapable of manufacturing this amino-acid. Another, deleterious effect of invasive tumours is their high cathepsin activity (Sylvèn and Malmgren, 1955), which digests materials from the tissues round them.

The problem of cell-differentiation in embryos has become even more closely linked in recent years with that of malignant transformation. Ever since Jacob and Monod promulgated their scheme (1961) for a mechanism of interaction between genes and cytoplasm, and since the mechanism of protein synthesis came to be explained in terms of RNA templates formed as a copy of base sequences in DNA, it has become much easier to understand how agents such as viruses, which consist almost entirely of nucleic acid, can transform cells. Can we, however, justifiably apply this kind of concept of transformation to explain the changes in embryonic cells? Can it be suggested that either RNA or DNA acts 'on the loose' like a virus, perhaps crossing from one tissue to another at moments when the tissues interact and influence each others' differentiation? There has been more than one claim (e.g. Steinberg, 1963) that the material extracted from between cells after they have been disaggregated ('intercellular material' or, in current jargon, 'ICM') contains DNA. Others (e.g. Curtis, 1958) have considered it to contain RNA. But no one has yet shown conclusively that whole nucleic acid molecules, or even sizeable nucleotides, pass from one tissue into another intact. All we have is the evidence that such molecules, or their larger combinates with proteins, for instance, can set off the chain of events that results in the formation of a neural plate, when they are implanted into a gastrula or explanted in a ball of ectoderm (Chapter Seven).

There are abundant reports in the recent literature (e.g. Bieber, 1954, Tencer, 1961) that analogues of nucleic acid derivatives, like many other metabolic analogues, cause abnormal development in amphibian embryos. The whole subject of metabolic inhibitors and competitive inhibition of metabolism by structural analogues has purposely been omitted from this book because there are still so many points of controversy as to how analogues act and, when it comes to experiments on embryos, there is often no certainty that the analogue is acting in any specific way other than blocking protein or nucleic acid synthesis as a whole. A useful survey of the literature on amino-acid analogues will be found in Herrmann's account (1960) of protein synthesis in embryonic cells. Many other, less specific, inhibitors have been used in numerous inconclusive experiments aimed at finding out which developmental processes most depend on a particular biochemical reaction or metabolite. Most of such work should, I feel, be kept in the category of 'teratology' at present: it is not yet informative enough for inclusion in 'orthodox' biochemical embryology. No real understanding of the basis of cell differentiation is likely to come from this 'inhibitory' approach; unless, like Jacobson (1964), we choose one particular cell-type and a very well-known metabolic pathway for study. More conclusive information will be obtained when we can devise systems such as those of Barth and Barth (1963) and Wilde (1955) in which a certain type of embryonic cell can be switched into several alternative courses of differentiation by adding a single, simple component to its culture medium. It is a pity that Wilde had not the courage or conviction to continue his work on the neural crest's dependence on phenylalanine. There must be many other such systems awaiting investigation: these tissue culture techniques are, moreover, simple enough to be mastered by both biochemists and biologists with little trouble.

In a previous review of the roles of amino-acids in the differentiation of animal cells (Deuchar, 1963 a) I incorporated Wilde's results, with some others, into a diagrammatic scheme, using the Jacob-Monod picture of the 'operon' as a starting-point and suggesting some of the influences that amino-acids or other small metabolites might exert on gene-products in embryonic cells. This, with the additional possibilities that have been mentioned in this book, is reproduced in more elaborate form in Fig. 10.20. Certainly we must still believe that cell differentiation in embryos is influenced by the properties of the cytoplasm, since it is not possible otherwise to explain the ability of late embryonic nuclei to behave in the same way as a zygote nucleus when transplanted back into an enucleated egg (p. 62), or the adverse effects of foreign egg cytoplasm in Moore's and Hennen's back-transfer experiments (p. 60). The nuclei cannot have changed permanently: they must, therefore, have reacted in some non-permanent way to agents from the cytoplasm. It should be noted that adult cell nuclei can also be affected by transfer to different cytoplasms. Scholtissek (1959) has shown that the base ratio of RNA in liver nuclei changes when they are placed in foreign (kidney) cytoplasm: such a change, if permanent, would of course lead to the specification of changed protein synthesis. Harris (1965) has also shown that nuclei transferred to another cell-type, making a heterokaryon, are capable of taking on the characteristics of the new cell. They can, for instance, resume DNA or RNA synthesis even if they had lost this function in their cell of origin.

The diagram of Fig. 10.20 leaves out one historic and far-reaching concept of embryonic development: that of the 'field' or quantitative 'gradient' which is believed to control so many features of embryonic

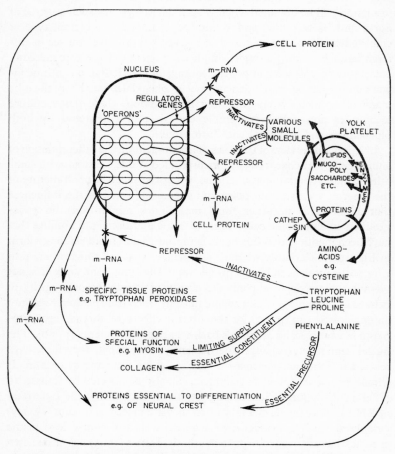

FIG. 10.20 Suggested effects of small molecules on some of the processes of differentiation in an embryonic cell.

topography. To bring this more into line with current interests, it seems most suitable to think of 'fields' arising after some, at least, of the cells involved have differentiated in response to their own or other cells' cytoplasmic inducers (cf. also Turing, 1952). When groups of cells start to interact, they can then be envisaged as building their own 'field' – as small in area as the somite, perhaps (cf. Fig. 8.5, p. 124), or as extensive as the head-tail gradient along the dorsal axis. The way to elucidate these somewhat philosophical concepts that early embryologists have handed down to us in their traditions, is to start our investigations at lower levels – the cell, or perhaps even the mitochondrion or, more typical of amphibian embryos, the yolk platelet. When we have discovered the mechanisms by which these small units are transformed, explanations of how they may interact to form a 'field' or 'gradient', then mediate 'inductions' on other cells according to this gradient, will not be so far off.

In the past, the amphibian egg may have seemed an *'enfant terrible'* to biochemists because of the extra difficulties it presented owing to its yolkiness and its constant changeability. In the present age of new ideas about cell-transformations and their genetic control, however, this giant embryonic cell deserves to become reinstated as favourite research material for the new generation of more biochemically-minded embryologists and more venturesome biochemists. Let us hope it will, anyway: there are still so many problems waiting to be solved in the biochemistry of amphibian development. The subject is still only in its embryonic stages.

References

AMBELLAN, E. (1958) 'Comparative effects of mono-, di-, and triphosphorylated nucleosides on amphibian morphogenesis.' *J. Embryol. exp. Morph.* **6**, 86–93.

AMBELLAN, E. and WEBSTER, G. (1962) 'Effects of nucleotides on neurulation in amphibian embryos.' *Develop. Biol.* **5**, 452–67.

ANSELL, G. B. and RICHTER, D. (1954) 'A note on the free amino-acid content of brain.' *Biochem. J.*, **57**, 70–3.

BAGLIONI, C. and SPARKS, C. E. (1963) 'A study of haemoglobin differentiation in *Rana catesbeiana.*' *Develop. Biol.* **8**, 272–85.

BAKER, P. C. (1965) 'Fine structure and morphogenetic movements in the gastrula of the treefrog, *Hyla regilla.*' *J. Cell Biol.* **24**, 95–116.

BALINSKY, B. I. (1960a) 'The role of cortical granules in the formation of the fertilization membrane and the surface membrane of fertilized sea urchin eggs.' *Symposium on Germ Cells and Development*, pp. 205–19.

BALINSKY, B. I. (1960b) 'Ultrastructural mechanisms of gastrulation and neurulation.' *Symposium on Germs Cells and Development*, pp. 550–63.

BALINSKY, B. I. (1960c) *An Introduction to Embryology.* Saunders: Philadelphia and London.

BALINSKY, B. I. and DEVIS, R. J. (1963) 'Origin and differentiation of cytoplasmic structures in the oocytes of *Xenopus laevis.*' *Acta Embryol. morph. Exp.* **6**, 55–108.

BALTUS, E. and BRACHET, J. (1962) 'Le dosage de l'acide desoxyribonucléique dans les oeufs de Batraciens.' *Biochim. Biophys. Acta* **61**, 157–63.

BARTH, L. G. (1941) 'Neural differentiation without organizer.' *J. exp. Zool.* **87**, 371–83.

BARTH, L. G. and BARTH, L. J. (1954) *The Energetics of Development.* Columbia University Press.

BARTH, L. G. and BARTH, L. J. (1963) 'The relation between intensity of inductor and type of cellular differentiation of *Rana pipiens* presumptive epidermis.' *Biol. Bull.* **124**, 125–40.

BARTH, L. G. and BARTH, L. J. (1964) 'Sequential induction of the presumptive epidermis of *Rana pipiens.*' *Biol. Bull.* **127**, 413–27.

BARTH, L. G. and JAEGER, L. J. (1947) 'Phosphorylation in the frog's egg.' *Physiol. Zool.* **20**, 133–46.

BARTH, L. G. and SZE, L. C. (1951) 'The organizer and respiration in *Rana pipiens*.' *Exp. Cell Res.* **2**, 608–14.

BARTH, L. J. (1956) 'Selective inhibition of cleavage in different regions of the frog egg by sulphydryl inhibitors.' *J. Embryol. exp. Morph.* **4**, 73–92.

BEAUMONT, A. (1954) 'L'apparition du glycogène hépatique chez les larves de Batraciens anoures.' *C.R. Soc. Biol: (Paris)*, **148**, 29–31.

BECKER, U. (1959) 'Die Bedeutung des reagierenden Gewebes für die Ausbildung von freien Linsengebilden bei *Triturus vulgaris*.' *Roux'Arch. Entw. Mech. Org.* **151**, 188–217.

BEERMAN, W. (1956) 'Nuclear differentiation and functional morphology of chromosomes.' *Cold Spr. Harb. Symp. Quant. Biol.* **21**, 217–32.

BELLAIRS, R. (1964) 'Biological aspects of the yolk of the hen's egg.' *Adv. Morph.* **4**, 217–72.

BENNETT, T. P. and FRIEDEN, E. (1962) 'Metamorphosis and biochemical adaptation in Amphibia.' *In: Comparative Biochemistry*, IV, pp. 483–556 (eds. Florkin and Mason).

BIEBER, S. (1954) 'Analogues of nucleic acid derivatives and the growth and development of *Rana pipiens*.' *J. Cell. Comp. Physiol.* **44**, 11–31.

BILLETT, F. (1957) 'β-glucuronidase activity during early development of *Xenopus laevis* embryos.' *Biochem. J.* **67**, 463–6.

BILLINGHAM, R. E., BRENT, L., and MEDAWAR, P. B. (1956) 'Quantitative studies on tissue transplantation immunity. III. Actively acquired tolerance.' *Phil. Trans. Roy. Soc. (B)*, **239**, 257–412.

BLACKLER, A. W. (1958) 'Contribution to the study of germ cells in the Anura.' *J. Embryol. exp. Morph.* **6**, 491–503.

BLOCK, R. J. and WEISS, K. W. (1956) *Amino-acid handbook*. Illinois: C. C. Thomas.

BOELL, E. J. (1948) 'Biochemical differentiation during animal development.' *Ann. N.Y. Acad. Sci.* **49**, 773.

BOELL, E. J. (1955) 'Energy exchange and enzyme development during embryogenesis.' *In: Analysis of Development*, pp. 520–55 (Willier, Weiss, and Hamburger, eds.). Saunders Co.

BOELL, E. J., GREENFIELD, P., and HILLE, B. (1963) 'The respiratory function of gills in the larvae of *Amblystoma punctatum*.' *Develop. Biol.* **7**, 420–31.

BOELL, E. J., GREENFIELD, P., and SHEN, S. C. (1955) 'Development of cholinesterase in the optic lobes of the frog (*Rana pipiens*).' *J. exp. Zool.* **129**, 415–51.

BOELL, E. J. and SHEN, S. C. (1950) 'Development of cholinesterase in the central nervous system of *Amblystoma punctatum*.' *J. exp. Zool.* **113**, 583–600.

BOELL, E. J. and WEBER, R. (1955) 'Cytochrome oxidase activity in mitochondria during amphibian development.' *Exp. Cell Res.* **9**, 559–67.

BOUNOURE, L. (1939) *L'origine des cellules reproductrices et le problème de la lignée germinale.* Gauthiers-Villars, Paris.

BOURNE, G. H. (1952) 'Autoradiography.' *Biological Reviews,* **27,** 108.

BRACHET, J. (1934) 'Etude du métabolisme de l'oeuf de Grenouille (*Rana fusca*) au cours du développement. 1. La respiration et la glycolyse de la segmentation à l'éclosion.' *Arch. Biol.* **45,** 611–727.

BRACHET, J. (1935) 'Etude du métabolisme de l'oeuf de Grenouille (*Rana fusca*) au cours du développement. 2. La respiration de l'oeuf pendant la fécondation et la mitose.' *Arch. Biol.* **46,** 1–45.

BRACHET, J. (1944) *Embryologie Chimique.* Masson et Cie, Paris.

BRACHET, J. (1954) 'Constitution anormale du noyau et métabolisme de l'embryon chez les Batraciens.' *Arch. Biol.* **65,** 1–72.

BRACHET, J. (1957) *Biochemical Cytology.* Academic Press, New York.

BRACHET, J. (1960) *The Biochemistry of Development.* Pergamon Press.

BRACHET, J. (1964) 'Effects of histones on embryonic development.' *Nature,* **204,** 1218–9.

BRACHET, J., DENIS, H. and DE VITRY, F. 'The effects of Actinomycin D and Puromycin on morphogenesis in amphibian eggs and *Acetabularia mediterranea. Devel. Biol.* **9,** 398–434.

BRACHET, J. and FICQ, A. (1965) 'Binding sites of C^{14}-Actinomycin D in amphibian ovocytes and an autoradiography technique for the detection of cytoplasmic DNA.' *Exp. Cell Res.* **38,** 153–9.

BRAHMA, S. K. (1958) 'Experiments on the diffusibility of the amphibian evocator.' *J. Embryol. exp. Morph.* **6,** 418–23.

BRANDT, E. E. and FINAMORE, F. J. (1963) 'Protein synthesis in frog eggs. II. Amino-acid activation and incorporation by isolated nucleoli.' *Biochim. Biophys. Acta,* **68,** 618–24.

BRIGGS, R., GREEN, E. U., and KING, T. J. (1951) 'An investigation of the capacity for cleavage and differentiation in *Rana pipiens* eggs lacking functional chromosomes.' *J. exp. Zool.* **116,** 455.

BRIGGS, R., SIGNORET, J., and HUMPHREY, R. R. (1964) 'Transplantation of nuclei of various cell types from neurulae of the Mexican axolotl (*Ambystoma mexicanum*).' *Develop. Biol.* **10,** 233–46.

BRISTOW, D. A. and DEUCHAR, E. M. (1964) 'Changes in nucleic acid concentration during the development of *Xenopus laevis* embryos.' *Exp. Cell Res.* **35,** 580–9.

BROWN, D. D. and GURDON, J. (1963) 'Absence of ribosomal RNA synthesis in the anucleolate mutant of *Xenopus laevis.' Proc. Nat. Acad. Sci. (N.Y.),* **51,** 139–46.

BROWN, D. D. and LITTNA, E. (1964a) 'RNA synthesis during the development of *Xenopus laevis,* the South African clawed toad.' *J. Mol. Biol.* **8,** 669–87.

BROWN, D. D. and LITTNA, E. (1964b) 'Variations in the synthesis of stable RNA's during oogenesis and development of *Xenopus laevis*.' *J. Mol. Biol.* **8**, 688–95.

BROWN, G. W. and COHEN, P. P. (1958) 'Biosynthesis of urea in metamorphosing tadpoles.' *In: The Biochemical Basis of Development*, pp. 495–513 (McElroy and Glass).

BURGESS, A. M. C. (1966) Ph.D. Thesis, University of London.

BURNET, F. M. (1956) *Enzyme, Antigen & Virus*. Cambridge University Press.

BUTSCHAK, G. (1960) 'Elektronenmikroskopische Untersuchung der Feinstrukturen des Zytoplasma früher Embryonalstadien von *Ambystoma mexicanum*.' *Acta Biol. Med. German*, **5**, 83–92.

CALLAN, H. G. (1964) 'Lampbrush chromosomes.' Int. Cong. for Cell Biol., abstr. **10**, in *Excerpt. Med.*, *Int. Cong.* series **77**, 12–13.

CASTON, J. D. (1962) 'Appearance of catechol amines during development of *Rana pipiens*.' *Develop. Biol.* **5**, 468–82.

CEAS, M. P. and NASELLI, A. (1958) 'Incorporation of S-35-methionine in developmental stages of *Discoglossus pictus*.' *Acta Embryol. Morph. Exp.* **1**, 207–10.

CHEN, P. S. (1953) 'The rate of oxygen consumption in the lethal hybrid between Triton ♀ and Salamandra ♂.' *Exp. Cell Res.* **5**, 275–87.

CHEN, P. S. (1956) 'Metabolic changes in free amino-acids and peptides during urodele development.' *Exp. Cell Res.* **10**, 675–86.

CHEN, P. S. (1960) 'Changes in DNA and RNA during embryonic urodele development.' *Exp. Cell Res.* **21**, 523–34.

CHEN, P. S. and ZELLER, CH. (1961) 'Changes in DNA and RNA during embryonic development of the merogonic combination *Triton palmatus* (♀) × *Triton cristatus* (♂).' *Experientia*, **17**, 177.

CLAYTON, R. M. (1953) 'Antigens in the developing newt embryo.' *J. Embryol. exp. Morph.* **1**, 25–42.

CLEMENTE, C. (1964) 'Regeneration in the vertebrate central nervous system.' *Annual Review of Neurobiol.* **6**, 258–93.

COGHILL, G. E. (1914) 'Correlated anatomical and physiological studies of the growth of the nervous system in Amphibia'. *J. Comp. Neurol.* **24**, 161–234.

COHEN, A. I. (1954) 'Studies on glycolysis during the early development of the *Rana pipiens* embryo.' *Physiol. Zool.* **27**, 128–41.

COHEN, S. (1958) 'A nerve growth-promoting protein.' *In: The Chemical Basis of Development*, pp. 665–76 (eds. McElroy and Glass).

COLEMAN, J. R. (1962) 'Deoxyribonuclease activities in the development of the leopard frog, *Rana pipiens*.' *Develop. Biol.* **5**, 232–51.

COONS, A. H. and KAPLAN, M. H. (1950) 'Localization of antigen in tissue cells. II. Improvements in a method for the detection of antigen by means of fluorescent antibody.' *J. exp. Med.* **91**, 1–14.

CRICK, F. H. C., BARNETT, L., BRENNER, S., and WATTS-TOBIN, R. J. (1961) 'General nature of the genetic code for proteins.' *Nature*, 192, 1227–32.

CURTIS, A. S. G. (1957) 'The role of calcium in cell aggregation of *Xenopus* embryos.' *Proc. Roy. Phys. Soc. (Edin.)*, 26, 25–32.

CURTIS, A. S. G. (1958) 'A ribonucleoprotein from amphibian gastrulae.' *Nature*, 181, 185.

CURTIS, A. S. G. (1960) 'Cortical grafting in *Xenopus laevis*.' *J. Embryol. exp. Morph.* 8, 163–73.

CURTIS, A. S. G. (1961) 'Timing mechanisms in the specific adhesion of cells.' *Exp. Cell Res. Suppl.* 8, 107–22.

CURTIS, A. S. G. (1962) 'Morphogenetic interactions before gastrulation in the amphibian *Xenopus laevis* – the cortical field.' *J. Embryol. exp. Morph.* 10, 410–22.

CURTIS, D. R., PHILLIS, J. W., and WATKINS, J. C. (1960) 'The chemical excitation of spinal neurons by certain acidic amino-acids.' *J. Physiol.* 150, 656–82.

DALCQ, A. M. (1960) *In: Fundamental Aspects of Normal and Malignant Growth* (ed. Nowinski). Elsevier Publ. Co.

DALTON, H. C. (1953) *In: Pigment Cell Growth*, pp. 17–28. Academic Press.

D'AMELIO, V. and CEAS, M. P. (1957) 'Distribution of protease activity in the blastula and early gastrula of *Discoglossus pictus*.' *Experientia*, 13, 152–3.

DAN, K. and KUJIYAMA, M. K. (1963) 'A study on the mechanism of cleavage in the amphibian egg.' *J. exp. Biol.* 40, 7–14.

DANIEL, J. F. and YARWOOD, E. A. (1939) 'Early embryology of *Triturus torosus*.' *Univ. Calif. Publ. Zool.* 43, 321–55.

DENIS, H. (1961) 'Recherche sur la différenciation protéique au cours du développement des Amphibiens.' *J. Embryol. exp. Morph.* 9, 422–45.

DENIS, H. (1964) 'Effets de l'actinomycine sur le développement embryonnaire. I. Suppression de la compétence de l'ectoderme et du pouvoir inducteur de la lèvre blastoporale.' *Devel. Biol.* 9, 435–57.

DETTLAFF, T. A. and DETTLAFF, A. A. (1961) 'On relative dimensionless characteristics of the development duration in embryology.' *Arch. de Biol.* 72, 1–16.

DETWILER, S. R. (1933) 'Further experiments upon the extirpation of Mauthner's neurones in amphibian embryos (*Amblystoma mexicanum*).' *J. exp. Zool.* 64, 415–31.

DEUCHAR, F M (1956) 'Amino-acids in developing tissues of *Xenopus laevis*.' *J. Embryol. exp. Morph.* 4, 327–46.

DEUCHAR, E. M. (1958a) 'Free amino-acid changes during cleavage in *Xenopus laevis* embryos.' *Exp. Cell Res.* 14, 84–7.

DEUCHAR, E. M. (1958b) 'Regional differences in catheptic activity in *Xenopus laevis* embryos.' *J. Embryol. exp. Morph.* **6**, 223–37.

DEUCHAR, E. M. (1960a) 'Adenosine triphosphatase activity in early somite tissue of the chick embryo.' *J. Embryol. exp. Morph.* **8**, 251–8.

DEUCHAR, E. M. (1960b) 'Relation between somite segregation rate and ATP-ase activity in early chick embryos.' Ibid., pp. 259–67.

DEUCHAR, E. M. (1961a) 'Enhancement of ATP-ase activity, somite segmentation rate and aggregation of somite cells of *Xenopus* embryos by treatment with ATP.' *Exp. Cell Res.* **23**, 21–8.

DEUCHAR, E. M. (1961b) 'Amino-acid activation in embryonic tissues of *Xenopus laevis*. I. Increased ³²P exchange between pyrophosphate and adenosine triphosphate in the presence of added L-leucine.' *Exp. Cell Res.* **25**, 364–73.

DEUCHAR, E. M. (1962) 'Amino-acid activation in embryonic tissues of *Xenopus laevis*. II. Hydroxamic acid formation in the presence of L-leucine.' *Exp. Cell Res.* **26**, 568–70.

DEUCHAR, E. M. (1963a) 'Amino-acids and differentiation in animal embryos.' *Symp. Soc. exp. Biol. XVII*, 'Cell Differentiation', pp. 58–73.

DEUCHAR, E. M. (1963b) 'Tracing amino-acids from yolk protein into tissue protein. I. Incorporation of tritiated leucine into oocytes and its distribution in the early embryo of *Xenopus laevis*.' *Acta Embryol. Morph. Exp.* **6**, 311–23.

DEUCHAR, E. M. (1964) 'Tracing amino-acids from yolk protein into tissue protein. II. Incorporation of tritiated L-proline from yolk into tissue protein in *Xenopus* embryos.' *Acta Embryol. Morph. Exp.* **7**, 49–60.

DEUCHAR, E. M. (1965) 'Biochemical patterns in early developmental stages of vertebrates.' Chap. 5 in *The Biochemistry of Animal Development*, vol. 1 (ed. R. Weber). Academic Press.

DEUCHAR, E. M. and BRISTOW, D. A. (1965) 'Changing base ratios in RNA from embryonic cells of *Xenopus laevis*.' *Nature*, **205**, 1321–2.

DEUCHAR, E. M., WEBER, R. and LEHMANN, F. E., (1957) 'Differential changes of catheptic activity in regenerating tails of *Xenopus* larvae, related to protein breakdown and total nitrogen.' *Helv. Physiol. Acta.* **15**, 212–29.

DE VINCENTIIS, M. (1954) 'Ulteriori indagini sull'organogenesi del cristallino.' *Riv. Biol.* **46**, 173–92.

DOLLANDER, A. (1956) 'La structure du cortex de l'oeuf de *Triton* observée sur coupes fines et ultrafines au microscope ordinaire, et au microscope electronique.' *Compt. Rend. Soc. Biol. (Paris)* **148**, 152–4.

DRAGOMIROV, N. I. (1936) 'Uber Induktion Sekundären Retina im Transplantierten Augenbecher bei *Triton* und *Pelobates*.' *Roux'Arch. EntwMech. Org.* **134**, 716–37.

EAKIN, R. M. (1963) 'Ultrastructural differentiation of the oral sucker in the treefrog, *Hyla regilla*.' *Develop. Biol.* 7, 169–79.

EAKIN, R. M. (1964) 'Actinomycin D inhibition of cell differentiation in the amphibian sucker.' *Zeit. f. Zellforsch.* 63, 81–96.

EAKIN, R. M., KUTSKY, P. B., and BERG, W. E. (1951) 'Protein metabolism of the amphibian embryo. III. Incorporation of methionine into protein of gastrulae.' *Proc. Soc. exp. Biol. N.Y.* 78, 502–4.

EAKIN, R. M. and LEHMANN, F. E. (1957) 'An electronmicroscopic study of developing amphibian ectoderm.' *Roux'Arch. EntwMech. Org.* 150, 177–98.

EDSTRÖM, J.-E., EICHNER, D., and EDSTRÖM, A. (1962) 'The ribonucleic acid of axons and myelin sheaths from Mauthner neurons.' *Biochim. Biophys. Acta.* 61, 178–84.

EDSTRÖM, J.-E. and GALL, J. G. (1963) 'The base composition of ribonucleic acid in lampbrush chromosomes, nucleoli, nuclear sap and cytoplasm of Triturus oocytes.' *J. Cell Biol.* 19, 279–84.

ETKIN, W. (1955) 'Metamorphosis.' Chapter in: *Analysis of Development* (Willier, Weiss, and Hamburger, eds.). Saunders Co., U.S.A.

FICQ, A. (1954) 'Analyse de l'induction neurale chez les Amphibiens au moyen d'organisateurs marqués.' *J. Embryol. exp. Morph.* 2, 194–203.

FICQ, A. (1960) 'Métabolisme de l'oogénèse chez les Amphibiens.' *In: Symposium on Germ Cells and Development*, Inst. Internat. d'Embryol. Baselli, pp. 121–40.

FINAMORE, F. J. (1955) 'RN-ase and DN-ase activities studied in early development of *Rana pipiens* by spectrophotometry.' *Exp. Cell Res.* 8, 533.

FINAMORE, F. J. and VOLKIN, E. (1961) 'Some chemical characteristics of amphibian egg ribonucleic acids.' *J. biol. Chem.* 236, 443–7.

FITCH, K. L. and MERRICK, A. W. (1958) 'The glycogen content of ovarian, body cavity, and uterine eggs of the frog, *Rana pipiens*.' *Exp. Cell Res.* 14, 644–6.

FLICKINGER, R. A. (1949) 'A study of the metabolism of amphibian neural crest cells during their migration and pigmentation *in vitro*.' *J. exp. Zool.* 112, 465–84.

FLICKINGER, R. A. (1956) 'The relation of PPP-ase activity to yolk platelet utilization in the amphibian embryo.' *J. exp. Zool.* 131, 307–32.

FLICKINGER, R. A. (1960) 'Formation, biochemical composition and utilization of amphibian egg yolk.' *In: Symposium on Germ Cells and Development*, Inst. Internat. d'Embryol., Baselli, pp. 29–48.

FLICKINGER, R. A. (1963) 'Iodine metabolism in thyroidectomised frog larvae.' *Gen. comp. Endocrinol.* 3, 606–15.

FLICKINGER, R. A. (1964) 'Sequential appearance of monoioidotyrosine, diiodotyrosine, and thyroxine in the developing frog embryo.' *Gen. comp. Endocrinol.* 4, 285–9.

FLICKINGER, R. A., HATTON, E., and ROUNDS, D. E. (1959) 'Protein transfer in chimaeric *Taricha-Rana* explants.' *Exp. Cell Res.* **17**, 30–4.

FLICKINGER, R. A. and STONE, G. (1960) 'Localization of lens antigens in developing frog embryos.' *Exp. Cell Res.* **21**, 541–7.

FOX, H. (1957) 'The effect of unilateral blockage of a pronephric duct upon the development of the pronephros in *Triturus helveticus.*' *J. Embryol. exp. Morph.* **5**, 274–82.

FOX, H. (1963) 'The amphibian pronephros.' *Quart. Rev. Biol.* **38**, 1–25.

FRIEDBERG, F. and EAKIN, R. M. (1949) 'Studies on protein metabolism of the amphibian embryo. I. Uptake of radioactive glycine.' *J. exp. Zool.* **131**, 307–32.

GALL, J. G. and CALLAN, H. G. (1962) 'H3-uridine incorporation in lampbrush chromosomes.' *Proc. Nat. Acad. Sci. N.Y.* **48**, 562–70.

GLASS, L. E. (1959) 'Immuno-histochemical localization of serum-like molecules in frog oocytes.' *J. exp. Zool.* **141**, 257.

GORDON, M. W. and RODER, M. (1953) 'Adaptive enzyme formation in the chick embryo.' *J. Biol. Chem.* **200**, 859–66.

GRANT, P. R. (1959) 'The synthesis of deoxyribonucleic acid during early embryonic development of *Rana pipiens.*' *J. Cell. Comp. Physiol.* **52**, 227–47.

GRANT, P. R. (1960) 'The effect of nitrogen mustard on nucleo-cytoplasmic interaction during amphibian development.' *In: Symposium on Germ Cells and Development* – Inst. Internat. d'Embryol. Baselli, Roma, pp. 483–502.

GRANT, P. R. (1965) 'Informational Molecules and Embryonic Development.' Chap. 9 *'The Biochemistry of Animal Development'* (ed. R. Weber), Academic Press.

GREGG, J. R. and BALLENTINE, R. (1946) 'Nitrogen metabolism of *Rana pipiens* during embryonic development.' *J. exp. Zool.* **103**, 143–68.

GREGG, J. R. and ORNSTEIN, N. (1952) 'Anaerobic ammonia production by amphibian gastrulae explants.' *Biol. Bull.* **102**, 22–4.

GROSS, J. (1964) 'Studies on the biology of connective tissues; remodelling of collagen in metamorphosis.' *Medicine*, **43**, 291–304.

GROVE, A. J. and NEWELL, G. E. (1944) *Animal Biology*. Univ. Tut. Press.

GURDON, J. B. (1960) 'The developmental capacity of nuclei taken from differentiating endoderm cells of *Xenopus laevis.*' *J. Embryol. exp. Morph.* **8**, 505–26.

GURDON, J. B. (1964) 'The transplantation of living cell nuclei.' *Advances in Morphogenesis* **4**, 1–43.

HAMA, T. and OBIKA, M. (1960) 'Pterin synthesis in the amphibian neural crest cell.' *Nature*, **187**, 326–7.

HARRIS, D. L. (1946) 'Phosphoprotein phosphatase, a new enzyme from the frog egg.' *J. biol. Chem.* **165**, 541–50.

HARRIS, H. (1965) 'Behaviour of differentiated nuclei in heterokaryons of animal cells from different species.' *Nature*, 206, 583–8.

HARRIS, T. M. (1964) 'Pregastrular mechanisms in the morphogenesis of the salamander *Ambystoma maculatum*.' *Develop. Biol.* 10, 247–68.

HAUROWITZ, F. (1965) 'Antibody formation and the coding problem.' *Nature*, 205, 847–51.

HELFF, O. M. (1928) 'Studies on amphibian metamorphosis, III.' *Physiol. Zool.* 1, 463–95.

HENNEN, S. (1963) 'Chromosomal and embryological analyses of nuclear changes occurring in embryos derived from transfers of nuclei between *Rana pipiens* and *Rana sylvatica*.' *Develop. Biol.* 6, 163–83.

HERRICK, C. J. (1914) *J. Comp. Neurol.* 24, 343–428. The medulla oblongata of larval Amblystoma.

HERRMANN, H. (1953) 'Interference of amino-acid analogues with normal embryonic development.' *J. Embryol. exp. Morph.* 1, 291–5.

HERRMANN, H. (1960) 'Molecular mechanisms of differentiation: an inquiry into the protein-forming system of developing cells.' *In: Fundamental Aspects of Normal and Malignant Growth*, pp. 495–545. Nowinski, ed. Elsevier Publ. Co.

HIBBARD, H. (1928) 'Contribution à l'étude de l'ovogénèse, de la fécondation et de l'histogénèse chez *Discoglossus pictus* Otth.' *Arch. Biol.* 38, 251–326.

HILDEMANN, W. H. (1962) 'Immunogenetic studies of amphibians and reptiles.' *Ann. N.Y. Acad. Sci.* 97, 139–52.

HOAGLAND, M. B., KELLER, E. B., and ZAMECNIK, P. C. (1956) 'Enzymatic carboxyl activation of amino acids.' *J. biol. Chem.* 218, 345–58.

HOFF-JØRGENSEN, E. and ZEUTHEN, E. (1952) 'Evidence of cytoplasmic deoxyribosides in the frog's egg.' *Nature*, 169, 245.

HOFFMANN-BERLING, H. (1954) 'Adenosintriphosphat als Betriebstoff von Zellbewegungen.' *Biochim. Biophys. Acta*, 14, 182–94.

HOLTFRETER, J. (1933a) 'Nachweis der Induktionsfähigkeit abgetöteter Keimteile. Isolations- und Transplantationsversuche.' *Arch. Entw-Mech. Org.* 128, 584–633.

HOLTFRETER, J. (1933b) 'Die totale Exogastrulation, eine Selbstablösung des Ektoderms vom Entomesoderm. Entwicklung und funktionelles Verhalten nervenlöser Organe.' *Arch. EntwMech. Org.* 129, 670–793.

HOLTFRETER, J. (1943) 'Properties and function of the surface coat in amphibian embryos.' *J. exp. Zool.* 93, 251–323.

HOLTFRETER, J. (1947) 'Neural induction in explants which have passed through a sublethal cytolysis.' *J. exp. Zool.* 106, 197–222.

HOLTZER, H., MARSHALL, J. M., and FINCK, H. (1957) 'An analysis of myogenesis by the use of fluorescent antimyosin.' *J. Biophys. Biochem. Cytol.* 3, 705–24.

HOPE, J., HUMPHRIES, A. A., and BOURNE, G. H. (1963) 'Ultrastructural studies on developing oocytes of the salamander *Triturus viridescens*. I. The relationship between follicle cells and developing oocytes.' *J. Ultrastr. Res.* **9**, 302–24.

HOPE, J., HUMPHRIES, A. A., and BOURNE, G. H. (1964a) 'Ultrastructural studies on developing oocytes of the salamander *Triturus viridescens*. II. The formation of yolk.' *J. Ultrastr. Res.* **10**, 547–56.

HOPE, J., HUMPHRIES, A. A., and BOURNE, G. H. (1964b) 'Ultrastructural studies on developing oocytes of the salamander *Triturus viridescens*. III. Early cytoplasmic changes and the formation of pigment.' *J. Ultrastr. Res.* **10**, 557–66.

HÖRSTADIUS, S. (1950) *The Neural Crest*. Oxford University Press.

HUGHES, A. F. W. (1937) 'Studies on the area vasculosa of the embryo chick. II. The influence of the circulation on the diameter of the vessels.' *J. Anat.* **72**, 1–17.

HUGHES, A. F. W. and TSCHUMI, P. A. (1958) 'The factors controlling the development of the dorsal root ganglia and ventral horn in *Xenopus laevis* (Daud).' *J. Anat.* **92**, 498–527.

HWAN SUN SUNG (1962) 'Relationship between mitochondria and yolk platelets in developing cells of amphibian embryos.' *Exp. Cell Res.* **25**, 702–4.

INOUE, K. (1961a) 'Precipitin reactions and developmental arrest by antisera in amphibian embryos.' *Develop. Biol.* **3**, 657–83.

INOUE, K. (1961b) 'Serologically active groups of amphibian embryos.' *J. Embryol. exp. Morph.* **9**, 563–85.

JACOB, F. and MONOD, J. (1961) 'Genetic regulatory mechanisms in the synthesis of proteins.' *J. Mol. Biol.* **3**, 318–56.

JACOBSON, W. (1964) 'Cellular injuries caused by folic acid antagonists and some corticosteroids.' *In: Ciba Symposium on Cellular Injury*, pp. 136–61 (ed. A. V. S. de Reuck and J. Knight).

JAEGER, L. J. (1945) 'Glycogen utilisation in the amphibian gastrula in relation to invagination and induction.' *J. cell. comp. Physiol.* **25**, 97–120.

JONES, K. W. (1965) 'The role of the nucleolus in the formation of ribosomes.' *J. Ultrastr. Res.* **13** 257–62.

JURAND, A. and SELMAN, G. G. (1964) 'Yolk utilisation in the notochord of newt as studied by electron microscopy.' *J. Embryol. exp. Morph.* **12**, 43–50.

KAIGHN, M. E. (1964) 'A biochemical study of the hatching process in *Fundulus heteroclitus*.' *Develop. Biol.* **9**, 56–80.

KALLÉN, B. (1956) 'Experiments on neurometry in *Ambystoma punctatum* embryos.' *J. Embryol. exp. Morph.* **4**, 66–72.

KARASAKI, S. (1959a) 'Electron microscope studies on cytoplasmic structures of ectoderm cells of the *Triturus* embryo during the early phase of differentiation.' *Embryologia* **4**, 247–72.

KARASAKI, S. (1959b) 'Changes in fine structure of the nucleus during early development of the ectoderm cells of the *Triturus* embryo.' Ibid. pp. 273–82.

KARASAKI, S. (1963a) 'Studies on amphibian yolk. I. The ultrastructure of the yolk platelet.' *J. Cell Biol.* **18**, 135–51.

KARASAKI, S. (1963b) 'Studies on amphibian yolk. 5. Electron microscopic observations on the utilisation of yolk platelets during embryogenesis.' *J. Ultrastr. Res.* **9**, 225–47.

KEMP, N. E. (1953) 'Synthesis of yolk in oöcytes of *Rana pipiens* after induced ovulation. *J. Morph.* **92**, 487–505.

KEMP, N. E. (1956a) 'Electron microscopy of growing oocytes of *Rana pipiens.*' *J. Biochem. Biophys. Cytol.* **2**, 281–91.

KEMP, N. E. (1956b) 'Differentiation of the cortical cytoplasm and inclusions in oocytes of the frog.' *J. Biochem. Biophys. Cytol.* Suppl. **2**, 187–92.

KEMP, N. E. and HIBBARD, E. (1960) 'Rate of incorporation of C-14-glycine injected into female adult frogs.' *J. exp. Zool.* **145**, 73–84.

KOCHER-BECKER, U., TIEDEMANN, H., and TIEDEMANN, H. (1965) 'Exovagination of newt endoderm: cell affinities altered by the mesodermal inducing factor.' *Science*, **147**, 167–9.

KOLLROSS, J. J. (1942) 'Localized maturation of the lid-closure reflex mechanism by thyroxin implants into tadpole hindbrain.' *Proc. Soc. exp. Biol.* **49**, 204–6.

KRUGELIS, E. J. (1950) 'Properties and changes of alkaline phosphatase activity during amphibian development.' *Compt. Rend. Lab. Carlsb.*, sér. chim. **27**, 273–90.

KURATA, Y. (1962) 'On the appearance of hydrogenase, nitrate reductase and aspartase during the ontogeny of the frog.' *Exp. Cell Res.* **28**, 424–9.

KUTSKY, P. B., EAKIN, R. M., BERG, W. E., and KAVANAU, J. L. (1953) 'Protein metabolism of the amphibian embryo. IV. Quantitative changes in free and non-protein amino-acids.' *J. exp. Zool.* **124**, 263–78.

KUUSI, T. (1958) 'The mesoderm in duction process in amphibians studied with the aid of radioactive tracers. I. Experiments with glycine-C-14.' II. Experiments with $Na_2S^{35}O_4$ and methionine-S^{35}. *Arch. Zool. Bot. Fenn.* '*Vanamo*', **13**, 97–105. **14**, 4–28.

LANG, C. A. and GRANT, P. R. (1961) 'Respiratory enzyme changes during frog embryogenesis.' *Proc. Nat. Acad. Sci. U.S.* **47**, 1236.

LANGMAN, J. and PRESCOTT, D. (1959) 'An immunological approach to the problem of lens regeneration.' *J. Embryol. exp. Morph.* **7**, 549–55.

LANZAVECCHIA, G. (1960) 'The yolk formation in frog oocytes. Electron microscope studies.' *In: Symposium on Germ Cells and Development.* Inst. Internat. d'Embryol. Baselli, pp. 61–74.

LAUFER, H. (1959) 'Immunochemical studies of muscle proteins in mature and regenerating limbs of the adult newt, *T. viridescens.*' *J. Embryol. exp. Morph.* **7**, 431–58.

LAVIN, L. (1963) 'Immunochemical studies of frog egg fertilization.' *Amer. Zoologist,* **3**, 119 (abstr.).

LEHMANN, F. E. (1954) 'Totale Regenerationshemmung am Schwanze der *Xenopus* larve.' *Rev. Suisse Zool.* **61**, 428–37.

LEE, N. D. (1956) 'The induced increase in the tryptophan peroxidase activity of rat liver: time studies.' *J. biol. Chem.* **219**, 211–20.

LEVI-MONTALCINI, R. (1958) 'Chemical stimulation of nerve growth' *Symposium on the Chemical Basis of Development* (McElroy and Glass) pp. 646–64. Johns Hopkins Press.

LEVI-MONTALCINI, R. (1964) 'Growth control of nerve cells by a protein factor and its antiserum.' *Science,* **143**, 105–10.

LOPASHOV, G. (1936) 'Eye inducing substances.' *Inst. exp. Biol. (Moscow).*

LØVTRUP, S. (1955) 'Chemical differentiation during amphibian embryogenesis.' *Compt. Rend. Trav. Lab. Carlsb. sér. chim.* **29**, 262–314.

LØVTRUP, S. (1959) 'On the causes of variations in the respiratory curves during amphibian embryogenesis.' *J. exp. Zool.* **140**, 231–46.

LØVTRUP, S. (1960) 'Biochemical indices of differentiation.' *From:* 4th International Congr. Biochem., vol. VI. *Biochemistry of Morphogenesis,* pp. 105–20.

LØVTRUP, S. (1962) 'On the surface coat in the amphibian embryo.' *J. exp. Zool.* **150**, 197–206.

LØVTRUP, S. (1962) 'Permeability changes in fertilized and activated amphibian eggs.' *J. exp. Zool.* **151**, 79–84.

LØVTRUP, S. and WERDINIUS, B. (1957) 'Metabolic phases during amphibian embryogenesis.' *J. exp. Zool.* **135**, 203–20.

LØVTRUP, S. and PIGON, A. (1958) 'Inversion of the dorso-ventral axis in amphibian embryos by unilateral restriction of oxygen supply.' *J. Embryol. exp. Morph.* **6**, 486–90.

MACGREGOR, H. C. (1965) 'The role of lampbrush chromosomes in the formation of nucleoli in amphibian oocytes.' *Quart. J. Micros. Sci.* **106**, 215–28.

MAISEL, H. and LANGMAN, J. (1961) 'Lens proteins in various tissues of the chick eye and in the lens of animals throughout the vertebrate series.' *Anat. Rec.* **140**, 183–93.

MANGOLD, O. and SEIDEL, F. (1927) 'Homoplastische und heteroplastiche Verschmelzung ganzer Tritonkeime.' *Roux'Arch. Entw-Mech. Org.* **III**, 341–422.

MARSHAK, A. and MARSHAK, C. (1954) 'Biological role of deoxyribonucleic acid.' *Nature,* **174**, 919–20.

MCKEEHAN, M. S. (1958) 'Induction of portions of the chick lens without contact with the eye cup.' *Anat. Rec.* **132**, 297–305.

N

MEISTER, A. (1956) 'The metabolism of glutamine.' *Physiol. Rev.* **36**, 103–27.

MEZGER-FPREED, L. and OPPENHEIMER, J. (1965). 'Ribonucleic acid base composition in the developing amphibian optic cup-lens system.' *Devel. Biol.* **11**, 385–401.

MONROY, A. (1965) *In: The Biochemistry of Animal Development*, Vol. I (ed. R. Weber). Academic Press.

MOORE, B. C. (1959) 'Autoradiographic studies of H3-thymidine incorporation in normal and hybrid frog embryos.' *Anat. Rec.* **134**, 610–11.

MOORE, B. C. (1963) 'Histones and differentiation.' *Proc. Nat. Acad. Sci.* **50**, 1018–26.

MOORE, J. A. (1960) 'Serial back-transfers of nuclei in experiments involving two species of frogs.' *Develop. Biol.* **2**, 535–50.

MOSS, B. and INGRAM, V. M. (1965) 'The repression and induction by thyroxin of haemoglobin synthesis during amphibian metamorphosis.' *Proc. Nat. Acad. Sci. N.Y.* **54**, 967–75.

MUNRO, A. F. (1939) 'Nitrogen excretion and arginase activity during amphibian development.' *Biochem. J.* **33**, 1957–65.

NACE, G. W. and LAVIN, L. (1964) 'Heterosynthesis and autosynthesis in the early stages of Anuran development.' *Amer. Zoologist*, **3**, 193–207.

NACE, G. W., SUYAMA, T., and SMITH, N. (1960) 'Early development of special proteins.' *In: Symposium on Germ Cells and Development*, pp. 564–603. Inst. Internat. d'Embryol. Baselli.

NASS, S. (1962) 'Localization and properties of phosphoprotein phosphatase in the frog egg and embryo.' *Biol. Bull.* **122**, 232–51.

NEEDHAM, A. E. (1952) *Regeneration and Wound Healing*. Methuen Monographs.

NEEDHAM, J. (1931) *Chemical Embryology*, Vol. II, reprinted Hafner, 1963.

NEEDHAM, J. (1942) *Biochemistry and Morphogenesis*, Cambridge Univ. Press.

NELSEN, O. E. (1953) *Comparative Embryology of the Vertebrates*. Blakiston, Toronto.

NEWTH, D. R. (1954) 'Determination in the cranial neural crest of the Axolotl.' *J. Embryol. exp. Morph.* **2**, 101–5.

NICHOLAS, J. S. (1945) 'Blastulation, its role in pregastrular organization in *Amblystoma punctatum*.' *J. exp. Zool.* **51**, 159–84.

NIEUWKOOP, P. D. and FABER, J. (1956) *Normal table of* Xenopus laevis (Daudin). North Holland Publ. Co., Amsterdam.

NIEUWKOOP, P. D. and FLORSCHÜTZ, P. (1950) 'Quelques charactères spéciaux de la gastrulation et de la neurulation de l'oeuf de *Xenopus laevis*, Daud. et de quelques autres Anoures. i. Étude déscriptive.' *Arch. Biol.* **61**, 113–50.

NIU, M. C. (1959) 'Current evidence concerning chemical inducers.' *In:*

Evolution of Nervous Control, pp. 7-30. Amer. Ass. Adv. Sci., Washington, D.C.

NIU, M. C. and TWITTY, V. (1953) 'The differentiation of gastrula ectoderm in medium conditioned by axial mesoderm.' *Proc. Nat. Acad. Sci. N.Y.* **39**, 985-9.

OBIKA, M. (1963) 'Association of pteridines with amphibian larval pigmentation and their biosynthesis in developing chromatophores.' *Develop. Biol.* **6**, 99-112.

OGAWA, Y. (1961) 'Effects of X-Ray irradiation on the synthesis of contractile proteins in *Triturus* embryos.' *Biochim. Biophys. Acta*, **54**, 397-9.

OGAWA, T. (1964) 'The influence of lens antibody on the lens regeneration in the larval newt.' *Embryologia*, **8**, 146-57.

OGAWA, T. (1965) 'Appearance of lens antigens during the embryonic development of the newt.' *Embryologia*, **8**, 345-61.

OHTSU, K., NAITO, K., and WILT, F. H. (1964) 'Metabolic basis of visual pigment conversion in metamorphosing *R. catesbeiana*.' *Develop. Biol.* **10**, 216-32.

ORNSTEIN, L. (1956) 'Mitochondrial and nucleolar interaction.' *J. Biochem. Biophys. Cytol.* Suppl. **2**, 351-2.

OSAWA, S. and HAYASHI, Y. (1953) 'Ribonucleic acid and protein in the growing oocytes of *Triturus pyrrhogaster*.' *Science*, **118**, 84-6.

OZBAN, N., TANDLER, C. J., and SIRLIN, J. L. (1964) 'Methylation of nucleolar RNA during development of the amphibian oocyte.' *J. Embryol. exp. Morph.* **12**, 373-80.

PANIJEL, J. (1950) 'L'organisation du vitellus dans les oeufs d'Amphibiens.' *Biochim. Biophys. Acta*, **5**, 343-57.

PANTELOURIS, E. M. (1958) 'Protein synthesis in newt oocytes.' *Exp. Cell Res.* **14**, 584-95.

PASTEELS, J. (1940) 'Un aperçu comparatif de la gastrulation chez les chordés.' *Biol. Rev.* **15**, 59-106.

PASTEELS, J. (1943) 'Fermeture du blastopore, anus et intestin caudal chez les Amphibiens anoures.' *Acta Neerl. Morph. A.* **5**, 11-25.

PASTEELS, J. (1961) 'La réaction corticale de fécondation ou d'activation. (Revue comparative.)' *Bull. Soc. Zool. France*, **86**, 600-29.

PETRUCCI, D. (1960) 'La citocromo-c-ossidasi nell'oogenesi degli Amfibi.' *Acta Embryol. Morph. exp.* **3**, 237-59.

PFAUTSCH, E. (1960) 'Untersuchung des Nukleinsäurengehaltes in verschiedenen Regionen bei der frühen Gastrula und Neurula von *Triturus alpestris* und *Ambystoma mexicanum*.' *Embryologia*, **5**, 139-69.

PICKFORD, G. (1943) 'The distribution of dipeptidase in the salamander gastrula.' *J. exp. Zool.* **92**, 143-70.

POLLOCK, M. R. (1959) 'Induced formation of enzymes.' *In: The Enzymes* (ed. Boyer, Hardy, and Myrback). Academic Press.

194   BIOCHEMICAL ASPECTS OF AMPHIBIAN DEVELOPMENT

QUINN, C. A. E. (1962) 'The antigenicity of regenerating tail tissue in the newt *Diemectylus viridescens*.' *Roux'Arch.* **154**, 160–70.

RANZI, S. (1962) 'The proteins in embryonic and larval development.' *Adv. Morph.* **2**, 211–59.

RAPKINE, L. (1931) 'Sur les processes chimiques au cours de la division cellulaire.' *Ann. Physiol.* **7**, 382–418.

RAVEN, CHR. P. (1954) *An Outline of Developmental Physiology.* Pergamon, London.

RAVEN, CHR. P. (1961) *Oogenesis: The Storage of Developmental Information.* Pergamon Press.

RINGLE, D. A. and GROSS, P. R. (1962) 'Organization and composition of the yolk platelet.' *Biol. Bull. Wood's Hole,* **122**, 263–97.

ROBERTS, E., LOWE, I. P., CHANIN, M., and JELINEK, B. (1957) 'Free or easily extractable amino-acids of heart muscle of various species.' *J. exp. Zool.* **135**, 239–54.

ROBERTS, E. and FRANKEL, S. (1949) 'Free amino-acids in normal and neoplastic tissues of mice, as studied by paper chromatography.' *Cancer Res.* **9**, 645–8.

ROMANOVSKY, A. (1964) 'Studies on antigenic differentiation in the embryonic development of *Rana temporaria* (L.). I. Agar precipitation tests. II. Ring test.' *Folia Biol.* **10**, 1–11 and 12–22.

ROSE, S. M. (1944) 'Methods of initiating limb regeneration in adult Anura.' *J. exp. Zool.* **95**, 149–70.

ROSENBAUM, R. M. (1958) 'Histochemical observations on the cortical region of the oocytes of *Rana pipiens*.' *Quart. J. Micros. Sci.* **99**, 159–69.

ROSENBAUM, R. M. (1960) 'Gastrular arrest and the control of autolytic activity in the egg of *Rana pipiens*: the comparative effects of oxygen, supramaximal temperature and dinitrophenol.' *Develop. Biol.* **2**, 427–45.

ROTHSCHILD, LORD and SWANN, M. M. (1949) 'The fertilization reaction in the sea-urchin egg. A propagated response to sperm attachment.' *J. exp. Biol.* **26**, 164–76.

ROUNDS, D. E. and FLICKINGER, R. A. (1958) 'Distribution of ribonucleoprotein during neural induction of the frog embryo.' *J. exp. Zool.* **137**, 479–500.

RUGH, R. (1951) *The Frog.* Blakiston Co., Toronto.

SALTHE, S. N. (1963) 'The egg capsules in the amphibia.' *J. Morph.* **113**, 161–71.

SALZMANN, R. and WEBER, R. (1963) 'Histochemical localisation of acid phosphatase and cathepsin-like activities in regressing tails of *Xenopus* larvae at metamorphosis.' *Experientia,* **19**, 352.

SAWYER, C. H. (1943) 'Cholinesterase and the behaviour problem in Amblystoma. III. The distribution of cholinesterase in nerve and muscle throughout development.' *J. exp. Zool.* **94**, 1–31.

SAXEN, L. and TOIVÖNEN, S. (1955) 'The development of the ultimo-branchial body in *Xenopus laevis* Daudin and its relation to the thyroid gland and epithelial bodies.' *J. Embryol. exp. Morph.* 3, 376–84.

SAXEN, L. and TOIVÖNEN, S. (1962) *Primary Embryonic Induction.* Logos, Academic Press.

SAXEN, L., SAXEN, E., TOIVÖNEN, S., and SALIMÄKI, K. (1957) 'Quantitative investigation on the anterior pituitary-thyroid mechanism during frog metamorphosis.' *Endocrinology,* 61, 35–44.

SCHECHTMAN, A. M. (1935) 'Mechanism of ingression in the egg of *Triturus torosus.*' *Proc. Soc. Exptl. Biol. Med.* 32, 1072–3.

SCHJEIDE, O. A., LEVI, E., and FLICKINGER, R. A. (1955) 'A study of the yolk proteins of frog eggs by physical and chemical means.' *Growth,* 19, 297–306.

SCHMIDT, A. J. and WEIDMAN, T. (1964) 'Dehydrogenases and aldolase in the regenerating forelimb of the adult newt, *Diemectylus viridescens.*' *J. exp. Zool.* 155, 303–16.

SCHOLTISSEK, C. (1959) 'Charaktisierung von Ribonucleinsaüren verschiedener Herkunft die gleiche Basenverhältnisse besitzen durch enzymatischen Abbau.' *Biochem. Zeit.* 331, 138–43.

SCHWIND, J. (1933) 'Tissue specificity at the time of metamorphosis in frog larvae.' *J. exp. Zool.* 66, 1–14.

SELMAN, G. G. (1958) 'The forces producing neural closure in amphibia.' *J. Embryol. exp. Morph.* 6, 448–65.

SELMAN, G. G. and PAWSEY, G. J. (1965) 'The utilization of yolk platelets by tissues of *Xenopus* embryos studied by a safranin staining method.' *J. Embryol. exp. Morph.* 14, 191–212.

SELMAN, G. G. and WADDINGTON, C. H. (1955) 'The mechanism of cell division in the cleavage of the newt's egg.' *J. exp. Biol.* 32, 700–33.

SENTEIN, P. (1961) 'L'action des antimitotiques pendant le segmentation de l'oeuf et le mécanisme de cette action.' *Pathol.-Biol.* 9, 445–66.

SENTEIN, P. (1963) 'Les structures figurées à mucopolysaccharides dans les ovocytes de Batraciens.' *Bull. de l'Ass. Anat., IIe. Reun.,* pp. 389–97.

SENTEIN, P. (1964) 'L'action de la vincaleucoblastine sur la mitose chez *Triturus helveticus* Raz.' *Chromosoma (Berl.)* 15, 416–56.

SHAFFER, B. M. (1963) 'The isolated *Xenopus laevis* tail: a preparation for studying the central nervous system and metamorphosis in culture.' *J. Embryol. exp. Morph.* 11, 77–91.

SINGER, M. (1952) 'The influence of the nerve in regeneration of the amphibian extremity.' *Quart. Rev. Biol.* 27, 169–200.

SINGER, M. (1959) 'The influence of nerves on regeneration.' *In: Regeneration in Vertebrates* (C. S. Thornton, ed.), pp. 59–80. Univ. of Chicago Press, Illinois.

SIRLIN, J. L. (1958) 'The labelling of mouse spermatozoa by adenine-8-^{14}C and thymidine-3H.' *Exp. Cell Res.* **15**, 250–3.

SIRLIN, J. L., BRAHMA, S. K., and WADDINGTON, C. H. (1956) 'Studies on embryonic induction using radioactive tracers.' *J. Embryol. exp. Morph.* **4**, 248–53.

SIRLIN, J. L. and WADDINGTON, C. H. (1954) 'Nuclear uptake of glycine-2-C-14 in the newt embryo.' *Nature,* **174**, 309.

SMITH, S. D. (1965) 'The effects of electrophoretically separated lens proteins on lens regeneration in *Dimectylus viridescens. J. exp. Zool.* **159**, 149–66.

SPEMANN, H. (1903) 'Uber Linsenbildung bei defekter Augenblase.' *Anat. Anz.* **23**, 457–64.

SPEMANN, H. (1938) *Embryonic Development and Induction.* (Reprinted.) Hafner, 1962.

SPIEGEL, M. (1954) 'The role of specific surface antigens in cell adhesion. II. Studies on embryonic amphibian cells.' *Biol. Bull.* (Wood's Hole), **107**, 149–55.

SPIEGEL, M. and FRANKEL, D. L. (1961) 'Role of enzyme induction in embryonic development.' *Science,* **133**, 275.

SPIEGEL, M. and SPIEGEL, E. S. (1964) 'The regulation of liver tryptophan pyrrolase activity during the development of *Rana catesbeiana.' Biol. Bull.* **126**, 307–18.

SPOFFORD, W. R. (1948) 'Observations on the posterior part of the neural plate in *Amblystoma.' J. exp. Zool.* **107**, 123–59.

STABLEFORD, L. T. (1949) 'The blastocoel fluid in amphibian gastrulation.' *J. exp. Zool.* **112**, 529–46.

STEARNS, R. N. and KOSTELLOW, A. B. (1958) 'Enzyme induction in dissociated embryonic cells.' *In: The Chemical Basis of Development* (McElroy and Glass, eds.), pp. 448–57. Johns Hopkins Press, Baltimore.

STEINBERG, M. S. (1963) ' "ECM": its nature, origin and function in cell aggregation.' *Exp. Cell Res.* **30**, 257–9.

STEINBERG, M. (1964) 'The problem of adhesive selectivity in cellular interactions.' *In: Cellular Membranes in Development,* pp. 321–66. Acad. Press.

STEVENS, L. C. (1954) 'The origin and development of chromatophores of *Xenopus laevis* and other Anurans.' *J. exp. Zool.* **125**, 221–46.

STONE, L. S. (1950) 'The role of retinal pigment cells in regenerating neural retinae of adult salamander eyes.' *J. exp. Zool.* **113**, 9–26.

STEEN, T. P. and THORNTON, C. S. (1963) 'Tissue interaction in amputated aneurogenic limbs of *Ambystoma* larvae.' *J. exp. Zool.* **154**, 207–22.

SWANN, M. and MITCHISON, J. M. (1958) 'The mechanism of cleavage in animal cells.' *Biol. Revs.* **33**, 103–65.

SYLVÈN, B. and MALMGREN, H. (1955) 'Topical distribution of proteo-lytic activities in some transplanted mice tumors.' *Exp. Cell Res.* **8**, 575-7.

SZE, L. C. (1953a) 'Changes in the amount of desoxyribonucleic acid in the development of *Rana pipiens.*' *J. exp. Zool.* **122**, 577-601.

SZE, L. C. (1953b) 'Respiration of parts of the *Rana pipiens* gastrula.' *Physiol. Zool.* **26**, 212-23.

TATA, J. A. (1965) 'Turnover of nuclear and cytoplasmic RNA at the onset of induced amphibian metamorphosis.' *Nature*, **207**, 378-81.

TEN CATE, G. (1959) 'The citric acid content of embryos of *Rana esculenta.*' *Experientia*, **15**, 57.

TEN CATE, G., KOOIJ, J. S., and ZUIDWEG, M. H. J. (1951) 'The effect of temperature on the synthesis of the enzyme cholinesterase in am-phibian embryos.' *Proc. Kon. Akad. Wetens.* (*C*) **54**, 1-16.

TEN CATE, G. and VAN DOORENMAALEN, W. J. (1950) 'Analysis of the development of the eye-lens in chicken and frog embryos by means of the precipitin reaction.' *Proc. Kon. Akad. Wetens.* **53**, 1-18.

TENCER, R. (1961) 'The effect of 5-fluorodeoxyuridine on amphibian embryos.' *Exp. Cell Res.* **23**, 418-19.

TIEDEMANN, H., KESSELRING, K., BECKER, U., and TIEDEMANN, H. (1961) 'The chemical nature of organ-determining substances in the early development of embryos.' *Biochim. Biophys. Acta*, **49**, 603-5.

TIEDEMANN, H., BORN, J. and KOCHER-BECKER, U. (1965) 'RNA syn-thesis and differentiation in amphibian embryos.' *Fed. Europ. Bio-chem. Socs.* (abstr.) c. 99.

TOOZE, J. and DAVIES, H. G. (1963) 'The occurrence and possible significance of haemoglobin in the chromosomal regions of mature erythrocyte nuclei of the newt, *Triturus cristatus.*' *J. Cell Biol.* **16**, 501-12.

TOWNES, P. L. and HOLTFRETER, J. (1955) 'Directed movements and selective adhesion of embryonic amphibian cells.' *J. exp. Zool.* **128**, 53-150.

TSCHUMI, P. (1956) 'Die Bedeutung der Epidermisleiste für die Entwick-lung der Beine von *Xenopus laevis* Daud.' *Rev. Suisse Zool.* **63**, 707-16.

TUFT, P. (1953) 'Energy changes in development.' *Arch. Neerl. Zool.* Suppl. **10**, 59-75.

TURING, A. M. (1952) 'The chemical basis of morphogenesis.' *Phil. Trans. B.* **237**, 37-72.

TWITTY, V. (1955) 'The Eye.' *In: Analysis of Development*, pp. 402-14 (Willier, Weiss, and Hamburger, eds.). Saunders Co.

TWITTY, V. C. and NIU, M. C. (1948) 'Causal analysis of chromatophore migration.' *J. exp. Zool.* **108**, 53-120.

URBANI, E. (1955) 'Gli enzimi proteolitici nella cellula, e nell'embrione.' *Experientia*, **11**, 209–18.

VAINIO, T., SAXÉN, L., and TOIVÖNEN, S. (1960) 'Transfer of the antigenicity of guinea-pig bone marrow implants to the graft tissue in explantation experiments.' *Experientia*, **16**, 27–8.

VECCHIOLI, A. (1956) 'Osservazioni sugli enzimi proteolitici durante lo sviluppo embrionale di *Bufo vulgaris*.' *Ric. Sci.* **26**, 2153–7.

VILMIKOVA, V. and NEDVIDEK, J. (1962) 'Changes in DNA content during early embryonic development of *Xenopus laevis* (Daudin) and *Rana temporaria* (L).' *Folia Biol.* **8**, 381–9.

WADDINGTON, C. H. (1952) 'Preliminary observations on the mechanism of cleavage in the amphibian egg.' *J. exp. Biol.* **29**, 484–9.

WADDINGTON, C. H. (1962) *New Patterns in Genetics and Development.* Columbia University Press.

WADDINGTON, C. H. and DEUCHAR, E. M. (1953) 'Studies on the mechanism of meristic segmentation. I. The dimensions of somites.' *J. Embryol. exp. Morph.* **1**, 349–56.

WADDINGTON, C. H. and PERKOWSKA, E. (1965) 'Synthesis of ribonucleic acid by different regions of the early amphibian embryo.' *Nature*, **207**, 1244–6.

WADDINGTON, C. H. and SIRLIN, J. L. (1954) 'The incorporation of labelled amino-acids into amphibian embryos.' *J. Embryol. exp. Morph.* **2**, 340–7.

WALLACE, H. (1962) 'Cytological studies of anucleolate *Xenopus* larvae. *Quart. J. Micr. Sci.* **103**, 25–35.

WALLACE, R. A. (1961) 'Enzymatic patterns in the developing frog embryo.' *Develop. Biol.* **3**, 486.

WALLACE, R. A. (1963a) 'Studies on amphibian yolk. III. A resolution of yolk platelet components.' *Biochim. Biophys. Acta* **74**, 495–504.

WALLACE, R. A. (1963b) 'Studies on Amphibian Yolk. IV. An analysis of the main-body component of yolk platelets.' *Biochim. Biophys. Acta*, **74**, 505–18.

WARD, R. T. (1962) 'The origin of protein and fatty yolk in *Rana pipiens*. 2. Electron microscopical and cytochemical observations of young and mature oocytes.' *J. Cell Biol.* **14**, 309–41.

WARNER, A. H. and FINAMORE, F. J. (1962). 'Nucleotide and nucleic acid metabolism in developing amphibian embryos – III. Metabolism of acid-soluble nucleotides.' *Comp. Biochem. Physiol.* **5**, 233–40.

WARTENBERG, H. (1962) 'Elektronenmikroskopische und Histochemische Studien über die Oögenese der Amphibienzelle.' *Zeit. f. Zellforsch.* **58**, 472–86.

WARTENBERG, H. (1964) 'Experimentelle Untersuchungen über die Stoffaufnahme durch Pinocytose während der Vitellogenese des Amphibienoocyten.' *Z. mikr. Anat. Forsch.* **63**, 1004.

WARTENBERG, H. and SCHMIDT, W. (1961) 'Elektronenmikroskopische Untersuchungen der Strukturellen Veränderungen im Rindenbereich des Amphibieneies im Ovar und nach der Befruchtung.' *Zeit. f. Zellforsch.* **54**, 118–46.

WEBER, R. (1957) 'On the biological function of cathepsin in tail tissue of *Xenopus* larvae.' *Experientia*, **13**, 153.

WEBER, R. (1962) 'Induced metamorphosis in isolated tails of *Xenopus* larvae.' *Experientia*, **18**, 84.

WEBER, R. (1964) 'Ultrastructural changes in regressing tail muscles of *Xenopus* larvae at metamorphosis.' *J. Cell Biol.* **22**, 481–7.

WEBER, R. and BOELL, E. J. (1955) 'Uber die Cytochromoxydaseaktivität der Mitochondrien von frühen Entwicklungsstadien des Krallenfrosches (*Xenopus laevis* Daud.).' *Rev. Suisse de Zool.* **62**, 260–8.

WEBER, R. and BOELL, E. J. (1962) 'Enzyme patterns in isolated mitochondria from embryonic and larvel tissues of *Xenopus*.' *Develop. Biol.* **4**, 452–72.

WEBER, R. and NIEHUS, B. (1961) 'Zur Aktivität der Saüren Phosphatase im Schwanz der *Xenopus*larven während Wachstum und Metamorphose.' *Helv. physiol. Acta*, **19**, 103–17.

WEIL-MALHERBE, H. (1953) 'Die Funktion der Glutaminsäure im Nervengewebe.' *Naturwiss.* **40**, 545–50.

WEISS, P. (1947) 'The problem of specificity in growth and development.' *Yale J. Biol. Med.* **19**, 235–78.

WEISS, P. (1955a) 'Nervous system' In: *Analysis of Development* (Willier, Weiss, and Hamburger, eds.), pp. 346–401. Saunders Publ. Co.

WEISS, P. (1955b) 'Specificity in growth control.' In: *Biological Specificity and Growth* (E. G. Butler, ed.). 12th Symp. Soc. Devel. Growth, pp. 195–206. Princeton U.P.

WEISS, P. and JACKSON, S. F. (1961) 'Fine-structural changes associated with lens determination in the avian embryo.' *Develop. Biol.* **3**, 532–54.

WEISZ, P. B. (1945) 'The normal stages in the development of the South African clawed toad, *Xenopus laevis*.' *Anat. Rec.* **93**, 161–70.

WIGGERT, B. O. and VILLEE, C. A. (1964) 'Multiple molecular forms of malic and lactic dehydrogenases during development.' *J. biol. Chem.* **239**, 444–51.

WILDE, C. E. (1955) 'The urodele neuroepithelium. II. The relationship between phenylalanine metabolism and the differentiation of neural crest cells.' *J. Morph.* **97**, 313–44.

WILDE, C. E. (1956) 'The urodele neuroepithelium. III. The presentation of phenylalanine to the neural crest by archenteron roof mesoderm.' *J. exp. Zool.* **133**, 409–40.

WILDE, C. E. (1960) 'The differentiation of vertebrate pigment cells.' *Advances in Morphogenesis*, **1**, 267–300.

WILLIAMS, J. (1965) *In: Biochemical Aspects of Development*, 1, Chap. 1 (ed. R. Weber). Academic Press.

WILLS, I. A. (1936) 'The respiratory rate of developing amphibia with special reference to sex differentiation.' *J. exp. Zool.* **73**, 481–510.

WILT, F. H. (1964) 'The role of enzymatic adaptation in embryonic differentiation.' *Amer. Nat.* **98**, 13–20.

WISCHNITZER, S. (1957) 'The ultrastructure of yolk platelets of amphibian oocytes.' *J. Biochem. Biophys. Cytol.* **3**, 1040–1.

WISCHNITZER, S. (1963) 'The ultrastructure of the layers enveloping yolk-forming oocytes from *Triturus viridescens*.' *Zeit. f. Zellforsch.* **60**, 452–62.

WITTEK, M. (1952) 'La vitellogénèse chez les Amphibiens.' *Arch. Biol.* **63**, 133–98.

WOERDEMAN, M. W. (1933) 'Uber den Glycogenstoffwechsel des Organisationszentrums in der Amphibiengastrula.' *Proc. Kon. Akad. Wetens.* **36**, 477–81.

WOERDEMAN, M. W. (1939) 'On lens induction.' *Proc. Konj. Akad. van Wetensch. Amsterdam*, **42**, 290–2.

YAMADA, T. (1958) Chapter on 'Embryonic Induction' *In: The Biochemical Basis of Development* (McElroy and Glass, eds.). Johns Hopkins Press.

YAMADA, T. (1960) 'A chemical approach to the problem of the organizer.' *Adv. Morph.* **1**, 1–53.

YAMADA, T. (1962) *In: The Cellular Basis of Differentiation. J. Cell. Comp. Physiol.* Suppl. **60**, pp. 49–64.

YAMADA, T. and TAKATA, K. (1961) 'A technique for testing macromolecular samples in solutions for specific effects on the isolated ectoderm of the amphibian gastrula.' *Develop. Biol.* **3**, 411–23.

YNTEMA, C. L. (1959) 'Blastema formation in sparsely innervated and aneurogenic forelimbs of *Amblystoma* larvae.' *J. exp. Zool.* **142**, 423–40.

ZEUTHEN, E. (1955) 'Mitotic respiratory rhythms in single eggs of *Psammechinus miliaris* and *Ciona intestinalis*.' *Biol. Bull. (Wood's Hole)*, **108**, 366–85.

ZOTIN, A. I. (1964) 'The mechanism of cleavage in amphibian and sturgeon eggs.' *J. Embryol. exp. Morph.* **12**, 247–62.

ZWILLING, E. (1960) 'Limb morphogenesis.' *In: Advances in Morphogenesis*, **1**, 301–28.

Index

fertilization, 11, 12, 50 ff.
Feulgen stain, 48
fibre tracts, 130
'field', 178–9
filters, 110, 116
fin, 30, 129
'fingerprints', 136
fishes, 101
fluorescent antibody methods, 36 ff.,
    49, 93, 98, 108 ff.
fluorimetry (of nucleotides), 169
folds, 113
follicle cells, 34 ff.
forebrain, 24–5
foreign cytoplasm effects, 59, 60
foreign proteins, 108
forelimb, 132–3
formylkynurenine, 94
fractionation method (Yamada), 102
free amino-acids, 74 ff., 96, 107, 145,
    169, 174–5
frog, 107
furrows (cleavage), 54 ff.

ganglia, see spinal ganglia
gastrulation, 17, 82 ff., 127, 161
germ layers, 15
germ plasm, 11
germinal vesicle, 36, 47
giant neurons, 25–6, 122, 130
gill, 32, 114, 129 ff., 137 ff.
globins, 137
glutamic acid, 64, 74–5
glutamine, 64, 74–5, 175
glycine, 75, 76, 107, 108
glycogen, 50, 96, 135, 158–9
Golgi body, 11, 40, 41
gonadotropin, 6, 38
gonads, 39
'gradient', 178–9
grey crescent, 11–12, 50, 61
guanidine, 71
guanidinetriphosphate (GTP), 80
guanine, 45
guinea-pig tissues, 103
gut, 17, 31–2, 127 ff., 135

haemoglobin, 3, 33, 95, 127, 136, 143,
    175
hanging-drop cultures, 109, 119
haploids, 122
hatching, 24 ff., 33, 128, 159
heart, 32, 74, 131, 133
heat shock, 87, 103, 104
heterokaryon, 177

hindbrain, 24
histochemistry, 67, 116, 142 ff.
histology, 66
histones, 163–4
homogenates, 167
homografts, 172
hormones, 139 ff., 164 ff.
hybrids, 158
hydrogenase, 169
hydroxyproline, 30, 79, 126
Hyla regilla, 92
hypertonic medium, 84
hypertrophy, 133, 134

immune system, 135, 172
immunological methods, 117
implantation, 98
induction, 98 ff., 111
information, 36
inhibitors, 49, 88, 176–7
inorganic ions, 111
insects, 101, 163
insulin, 135–6
intercellular material (ICM), 176
intestine, 31
invagination, 17, 65, 88, 114
iodine, 132, 140
iris, 117
isocitric dehydrogenase, 155
iso-enzymes, 3, 112

Jacob–Monod scheme, 63, 110
jelly capsule, 10, 33, 55, 129

kathepsin, see cathepsin
kidney, 17, 22, 103, 114, 130 ff., 177
kynurinene, 94

lactate, 158
lactate dehydrogenase, 3, 49, 112, 136,
    146, 158
lactic acid, 144
lampbrush chromosomes, 47–8, 163
larva, 75, 78, 129 ff., 136, 143
lens, 27, 115 ff.
leucine, 74 ff., 95, 125, 178
leucine-activation, 95–6
leucine uptake, 96
limb epidermis, 146
limb regeneration, 143 ff.
lipovitellin, 42–3
lithium chloride, 79, 106, 111–12
liver, 32, 37, 94, 103
lungs, 133
lymphocytes, 135

phosphatase, acid, 142–3, 154, 159
phosphatase, alkaline, 146, 159, 168
phosphate exchange, 89
phosphoprotein phosphatase (PPP-ase), 42, 44, 50, 63, 173
phosvitin, 42–3
pigment, 13, 34, 38 ff., 62, 111, 117–18, 120, 130–1
pinocytosis, 36
pineal gland, 25
pituitary gland, 24, 25, 33, 131, 141
placode stage, 117
platelets, see yolk
Pleurodeles waltlii, 48, 49, 59
poikilothermy, 5
polar body, 12, 35
polarized light, 54, 55
polymerase (DNA-), 58
polysaccharide, 44, 51
polyvinyl pyrollidone (PVP), 46
porphyropsin, 131, 137
precursors of phenylalanine, 119
pregastrulation movements, 14–15
proline, 30, 79, 96, 125–6, 178
pronephros, 130, 134
protease, 44, 103, 144
protein breakdown, 93
proteins, 48 ff., 72–4, 100, 108, 151–2, 167
puffs, 163

radial, see cleavage
radial nerve, 106
radioactive tracer work, 40, 76, 80, 98, 107 ff., 146
Rana catesbeiana, 135–7
Rana esculenta, 155
Rana pipiens, 36, 48, 50–1, 58, 60, 151, 158–9
Rana platyrrhina, 58
Rana sylvatica, 60
re-aggregation, 20, 87, 91
recapitulation, 168–9
regeneration, 117, 143–8
regional differences, 64, 66 ff.
regional differentiation, 104–5
regression phase of regeneration, 145
regulator locus, 63, 178
repressors, 63, 111, 178
reptiles, 101
respiration, 89, 92, 112, 145, 150–4
respiratory enzymes, 154–9
retina, 28, 117–18, 131, 141
retinene, 137
rhodopsin, 131, 137

ribonucleic acid (RNA), 38 ff., 44 ff., 58, 70, 80, 87, 92 ff., 103, 116, 159
base composition, 70, 72, 117, 122
messenger, 49, 59, 63, 109–10, 163
nucleolar, 46–7
on lampbrush chromosomes, 48
ribosomal, 45, 110, 117, 164
soluble, 44, 47, 110
time curves compared, 164–7
turnover, 47
ribonuclease (RNA-ase), 58–9, 103
ribonucleoprotein, 100, 110, 116
Rohon–Beard cells, 25–6

salamander sp., 100, 107, 122, 158
Salamandra atra, 158
saline medium, 105
scar tissue, 147
scatter diagram, 150
Schwann cells, 23, 121
sclerotome, 22, 30, 125–6
segmentation, 22–3, 123–5
selective adhesion, 88
selective uptake of amino-acids, 111
'self' and 'non-self', 134
sequential induction, 111
serological investigations, 36, 49, 117, 170–1
skeleton, 29, 131
skin, 133, 143
small metabolites, 37, 112, 169, 178
snake venom, 121
sodium radioactive tracer, 128
somites, 17–18, 22, 32, 77, 114, 123–5
specific proteins (tissue-), 109
Spek's theory of cleavage, 83
Spemann's ligation experiment, 4, 61–2
spinal ganglia, 23
spinocaudal induction, 104–5
stages of development (Xenopus), 7 ff.
statistical variance, 164
sterols, 100
stomach, 31
streptomycin sulphate, 100
stump, 145
subcortical zone, 56
substrate affinity, 144, 161
substrates, 169
succinic dehydrogenase, 146, 159
succinoxidase, 155
sucker, 114, 131
sulphocyanide, 79
sulphur-containing proteins, 79
sulphydryl groups, 57, 65, 73, 89, 136